W9-CYY-744

Long-Term Care
for the
Rural Elderly

Graham D. Rowles, PhD, is Professor of Geography and Behavioral Science and Associate Director of the Sanders-Brown Center on Aging at the University of Kentucky. He is a graduate of Bristol University (England) and Has a Ph.D. from Clark University (Massachusetts). His research focuses on the experience of aging in different environmental contexts. A central theme of this work is exploration, employing qualitative methodologies of the changing relationship between elderly people and their environment with advancing age, and the implications of this relationship for health and well-being. He has conducted in-depth ethnographic research with elderly populations in urban (inner city), rural (Appalachian) and nursing home environments. His publications include *Prisoners of Space? Exploring the Geographical Experience of Older People* and two co-edited volumes, *Aging and Milieu: Environmental Perspectives on Growing Old* and *Qualitative Gerontology*, in addition to 48 monographs, book chapters, and articles. Dr. Rowles is a Fellow of the Gerontological Society of America and serves on the editorial board of the *Journal of Gerontology (Social Sciences)*. He is currently editor of the *Journal of Applied Gerontology*.

Joyce E. Beaulieu, PhD, is in private practice as a health management and policy analyst and is owner of JB Associates, Health Management Consultants in Lexington, Kentucky. She was formerly Associate Professor of Health Administration and Public Administration, and a Faculty Associate of the Center for Rural Health and the Sanders-Brown Center on Aging at the University of Kentucky. Dr. Beaulieu holds a masters degree from the University of Rochester and a Ph.D. in Health Services Organization and Policy from the University of Michigan. Her primary areas of research are rural long-term care, home- and community-based alternatives, and Medicaid program evaluation. Her recent publications include a co-edited book on rural health. *Rural Health Services: A Management Perspective.*

Wayne W. Myers, MD, is the founding Director of the University of Kentucky Center for Rural Health in Hazard, which also serves as Kentucky's Office of Rural Health. He is a graduate of the University of Rochester School of Medicine with pediatric residency training at Rochester and the University of Colorado. He became interested in rural health care personnel and delivery systems during 17 years in Fairbanks, Alaska where he directed the Alaska component of the University of Washington's Washington, Alaska, Montana, Idaho (WAMI) Medical Education Program and was heavily involved in health planning and system development through the pipeline boom. Before coming to Kentucky in 1990 he served for 6 years as Associate Dean for Area Health Education Centers (AHEC's) in the four WAMI states and rural service programs within the Medical School.

Long-Term Care
for the
Rural Elderly

New Directions in Services,
Research, and Policy

Graham D. Rowles
Joyce E. Beaulieu
Wayne W. Myers

Editors

SPRINGER PUBLISHING COMPANY

Springer Publishing Company, Inc.
536 Broadway
New York, NY 10012-3955

Cover desigh by Margaret Dunin
Production Editor: Pamela Lankas

96 97 98 99 00 / 5 4 3 2 1

Library of Congress Cataloging-in-Publication Data

Long-term care for the rural elderly: new directions in services,
   research, and policy / Graham D. Rowles, Joyce E. Beaulieu,
   Wayne W. Myers, editors
       p.   cm.
   Includes bibliographical references and index.
   ISBN 0-8261-9380-3
   1. Aged—Long-term care—United States.   I. Rowles. Graham D.
II. Beaulieu, Joyce E.   III. Myers. Wayne W.
RAG44.6.L6617   1996
362. 1'6—dc20   96-28439
                                                          CIP

Printed in the United States of America

Contents

Foreword

It is not only good to have, finally, a reference source on long-term care in rural America, but it is really outstanding to have such a distinguished group of authors bringing together their research and policy expertise as well as their commitment to rural America in this single and singular book. As many of these authors point out, there is little material on long-term care system options in urban or rural settings, less material on rural aging and rural health care, and previously, virtually nothing on long-term care system options appropriate to aging rural Americans. This book makes a major contribution toward filling this gap in the rural research and policy literature.

Although each of the chapters focuses on a single element and its particular potential for rural Americans within the long-term system now, and into the next century, they have produced a cohesive whole across these elements. No doubt, this is possible, in part, because of their long-standing commitment to aging in rural America and their sensitivity to the culture of rural America. However, it is also strengthened by their shared philosophical underpinnings that rurality is not (nor should be) diminutive urbanism; that rural long-term care system solutions must be community-specific within a context of both rural elders' needs and rural culture; and that consumer, community, service provider, researcher, and policy advocates must become empowered and politically active in the debates on reorientation and reorganization of health care, and specifically long-term care, in a rural American context. If they do not, further fragmentation and rigidity will ensue with the current dreadful nonsystem, or worse, being carried into the twenty-first century.

Although Chapter 2 explicitly identifies obstacles or "challenges" to delivering long-term care in rural America, all of the authors have dealt, to some extent, with these issues. The major challenges discussed, with all of which I concur, are low population density and high dependency ratios; long and often arduous travel to services; shortages of trained and experienced personnel; lack of program and service coordination; fiscal constraints coupled with regulatory or reimbursement rigidity; and the lack of consumer and community empowerment or political advocacy. Most of the authors have also found strengths in rural long-term care in spite of the existing fragmented nonsystem. Notable among these strengths are the "ethos of neighborliness" (see Stoller); the sense of community within the nursing home (see Rowles) and the hospital (see Schlenker and Shaughnessy), producing an easy transition into and out of these facilities; and often higher quality to the services than is found in urban centers.

In looking to the future, Chapter 9 calls for rural long-term care systems with the following characteristics: (1) local community control, sensitive to and compatible with the local rural culture; (2) models of care that are, at least, bidirectional as opposed to the current unidirectional models based only on deterioration; (3) philosophies of care that are client-centered and, by extension, of decision making that respects the clients' informal supports and are family-centered; (4) integral cooperation among all service providers, based on explicit interdependence and reciprocity; (5) redefined health care roles and training of provider personnel; and (6) seamless construction of, and centralized access to client and resource data. Although Coburn (see Chapter 8) adds to these characteristics, the necessity for rural Americans to become their own advocates for rural long-term care system, by being or becoming politically active on their own behalf. These tenets set forth an agenda that will be difficult to attain but, which the authors and I believe, can be accomplished by building on the strengths of rural America.

The cohesiveness of the full text that is so strongly identifiable in Chapter 9 enhances the reading of Chapters 3 through 7 particularly. Therefore, I would urge readers to deviate from the usual reading of a text by reading Chapter 1, then Chapter 9, followed by Chapter 2 through 8, and then return to Chapter 9.

There are several key concepts that emerge throughout the text that convey powerful and positive messages throughout this important work. I have chosen to highlight these concepts here, almost in the fashion of listing keywords. These concepts include as the foremost--flexibility; reciprocity, especially functional reciprocity; interdependence; permeability of boundaries; innovativeness; and creativity. These are hallmarks of this book, but more important, they are clearly hallmarks of rural America as it develops its own solutions to providing appropriate long-term care to aging rural Americans through creative, interactive, comprehensive, and coordinated long-term care system as we move into the new millenium.

BETTY HAVENS
D. LITT.

Acknowledgments

This book comprises one component of a rural long-term care research, evaluation, and information-dissemination project that has spanned several years and has benefitted from enthusiastic and unselfishly given support from many people. We are indebted to a perceptive, hardworking and committed group of speakers who contributed to the conference that was the genesis of this book. In addition to those whose work appears in the following pages, the conference was enriched by the presentations of: Forrest W. Calico, President of Appalachian Regional Healthcare Inc.; Jeffrey Human, Director of the Federal Office of Rural Health Policy; Linda J. Redford, Director, National Resource Center on Rural Long-Term Care; William D. Remmes, Administrator, Roanoke Amaranth Community Health Group Inc.; and Elizabeth A. Selk, Executive Director, Alzheimer's Association of East Central Iowa. We would also like to express our appreciation for the efforts of Deborah D. Danner, Conference Director, for her organizational and administrative skills and acumen in moving the conference from an idea to reality and playing a leading role in associated research and information-dissemination activities. Deborah's efforts were aided by input from a conference advisory committee that was extremely active and involved in designing the conference. Members of this advisory committee were: Kimberly Emmett, Louise Howell, Linda C. Kuder, James C. Norton, Leslie Rogers, Sue Tuttle, and John Underwood. Thanks are also due to Malcolm C. Cutchin, Carole M. Gallaher, Evy Whitlatch, Jim Concotelli, and Mary Doole for their untiring efforts, equanimity, and good humor in producing resource materials and taking care of myriad administrative arrangements necessary to ensure the success of a major conference.

We are indebted to the Agency for Health Care Policy and

Research, which provided major funding to support the entire rural long-term care project of which this book is but a part (Grant No. AHCPR 1 R13 HS 08125). Financial support was also provided by Lee Magid, Vice President for Research and Graduate Studies at the University of Kentucky.

Preparation of this book was greatly facilitated by the critical reviews of early drafts of individual chapters that were received from a group of extremely diligent and insightful reviewers including: B. Jan McCulloch, Mark A. Davis, Linda C. Kuder, James C. Norton, David Green, Floyd Davis, John Underwood, and Loyd Kepferle. Finally, special thanks are due to Mary Carr who, in addition to playing a major role in the organization and administration of the conference, spent many hours working with contributors in clarifying aspects of each chapter and assumed primary responsibility for preparation of the final manuscript.

Contributors

Andrew Coburn, PhD, is Director at the Maine Rural Health Research Center and Edmund S. Muskie Institute of Public Affairs and Associate Professor of Health Policy Management at the University of Southern Maine in Portland, Maine.

Raymond T. Coward, PhD, is Professor of Health Policy and Epidemiology, Affiliate Professor of Sociology, Director of the Center on Rural Health and Aging, and Associate Director of the Institute for Health Policy Research at the University of Florida Health Science Center in Gainesville, Florida.

John A. Krout, PhD, is Professor of Sociology and Health Services Administration and Director at the Gerontology Institute of Ithaca College in Ithaca, New York.

Joan K. Magilvy, PhD, RN, is Associate Professor at the University of Colorado Health Sciences Center School of Nursing in Denver, Colorado.

Julie K. Netzer, PhD, is an Agency for Health Care Policy and Research (AHCPR) Postdoctoral Fellow in the Center on Rural Health and Aging and the Institute for Health Policy Research at the University of Florida Health Science Center in Gainesville, Florida.

Chuck W. Peek, PhD, is an Agency for Health Care Policy and Research (AHCPR) Postdoctoral Fellow in the Center on Rural Health and Aging and the Institute for Health Policy Research at the University of Florida Health Science Center in Gainesville, Florida.

Robert E. Schlenker, PhD, is Associate Director of the Center for Health Services and Policy Research at the University of Colorado Health Sciences Center and is Associate Professor in the Department of Medicine. He also codirects the Agency for Health Care Policy and Research Rural Center for Federal Region VIII.

Peter W. Shaughnessy, PhD, is Director for the Center for Health Services Research at the University of Colorado Health Sciences Center and is a member of the faculty of the School of Medicine of the University of Colorado Health Sciences Center.

Eleanor P. Stoller, PhD, is Professor of Health Policy in the Department of Health Policy and Epidemiology of the College of Medicine at the University of Florida in Gainesville, Florida.

Introduction: Long-Term Care for the Rural Elderly: The Legacy of the Twentieth Century

1

Graham D. Rowles
Joyce E. Beaulieu
Wayne W. Myers

As older rural Americans and their families strive to obtain the best possible care, to maximize their independence and minimize dollar costs of dependence, they are confronted with a long-term care system with critical gaps in programs and services. Moreover, in many rural areas, the partial, fragmented, and uncoordinated hodge-podge of long-term care that has developed in recent decades is unattuned to the changing needs and preferences of rural residents and insensitive to the culture of rural America. This book isolates dimensions of the problem and explores contemporary and future directions in the evolution of rural long-term care. Our contributors, representing disciplines ranging from geography through sociology, social work, nursing, and medicine, to health services research and policy studies, argue that rural long-term care is currently undergoing significant change as new options are introduced and rural institutions adapt to the evolving circumstances of rural America.

In this climate of change, we provide a review of the current status of rural long-term care—the legacy of the 20th century—and trace several contemporary trends in rural long-term care philosophy, programs, and policies. These trends can guide us toward the creation of more appropriate rural long-term care systems as we move into the 21st century. In this context, long-term care is broadly defined as "a set of health, personal care and social services delivered over a sustained period of time to persons who have lost or never acquired some degree of functional capacity" (Kane & Kane, 1987, p. 4). Thus, our concern is not only with the availability of appropriate health care options but also with social services and other types of both formal and informal support that enrich the quality of life of the rural elderly as they accommodate to increasing frailty. Our aim is to provide a holistic perspective on long-term care that views each individual service or institutional option as, ideally, part of a comprehensive and fully integrated system of care with the capacity to provide for the changing needs of each individual as his or her health and personal circumstances change.

The origins of the book lie in a national conference funded by the Agency for Health Care Policy and Research, "Long-Term Care for the Rural Elderly," held in Lexington, Kentucky, in the Fall of 1994, shortly after the conclusion of the major national debate on health care reform that dominated the 103rd Congress. The five overlapping objectives of the conference were:

1. Summarize the latest research on the availability of long-term care in rural areas, the changing role of specific rural institutions in providing long-term care, and distinctive social and cultural factors affecting contemporary rural long-term care practice.

2. Provide a forum for sharing information on innovative long-term care options in rural settings and evaluating the generalizability of these options to other rural contexts.

3. Explore ways in which the resources and potential of existing rural community institutions (the family, home- and community-based programs, senior centers, nursing homes, and hospitals) might be more fully utilized in developing an

integrated and responsive rural long-term care system.

4. Develop an agenda and strategies for research and the testing and implementation of new models of rural long-term care.

5. Assemble, integrate and disseminate information on rural long-term care (Rowles, Beaulieu, & Myers, 1994).

Each chapter in this volume was originally developed for distribution prior to the conference and for discussion by conference participants. Each contribution integrates feedback received from the conference audience and an additional critical review by two independent reviewers. Chapters are presented in a thematic progression from an emphasis on diagnosis of constraints and barriers to effective rural long-term care to a focus on remedies and strategies for improving the situation.

We begin with a description of the inadequacies of long-term care provision in rural America and critical assessment of major obstacles to the development of an effective rural long-term care system (Chapter 2). Coward, Netzer and Peek explain how, despite evidence of equal or greater need, long-term care services tend to be less available in rural than in urban areas. Low population density, lengthy travel distances, chronic shortages of trained personnel, lack of coordination among existing programs, and a variety of fiscal and political constraints, all combine to deny rural elders and their families equal access to the kinds of support available to their peers in most metropolitan areas.

In the chapters that follow, these themes provide a constant backdrop to consideration of the role and potential of specific rural community institutions to contribute to the development of a comprehensive and context-sensitive long-term care system. In Chapter 3, Eleanor Stoller explores the role of family in providing long-term care. She notes a greater reliance on informal sources of support and the ethos of neighborliness that pervades many rural areas. More important, she reveals a number of subtle dimensions of the caregiving relationship that typically function in this setting: "mixed configurations" of support in which informal support is supplemented by judiciously selected formal services, complex issues of dependence and interdependency, concerns about privacy

versus control, issues of reciprocity, and the meaning of caregiving. The family emerges as a critical resource in contemporary
rural long-term care.

With increasing frailty there often develops a need for services
that exceed what can be provided by the family. Joan Magilvy
(Chapter 4) focuses on the proliferation of home care and community-based service options that have emerged in response to this
need. While there are many options providing the potential for a
comprehensive system of care, the "uneven nature of community-
based care" (different combinations of long-term care resources in
different rural areas) is such that many rural areas are lacking in
needed services. In addition, programmatic and institutional constraints limit the ability of elders to move easily from one level of
care to another at "critical transition points" in their need for care.
Magilvy concludes that "creative vision" is needed to enable us to
progress toward more comprehensive and needs-sensitive systems
of home- and community-based care.

One option for focusing the development of such a comprehensive system is the rural senior center. In Chapter 5, Krout considers
the senior center as a fulcrum for the development and administration of rural long-term care programs and services. He notes
that the clientele of rural senior centers has become older and more
frail in recent years and that many senior centers have already
begun to provide or to coordinate extensive long-term care services, moving from a recreational to a service delivery focus. His
chapter suggests an exciting potential for rural senior centers to
become critical components of rural long-term care systems as
they "reinvent" themselves through examination of the fundamental roles they play in their communities.

As Rowles (Chapter 6) points out, in many rural areas the primary long-term care resource is the local nursing home. His ethnographic account of one such facility in rural Appalachia illustrates
the way in which a rural nursing home may remain very much
integrated within its community context by virtue of its history, its
close economic relationship to the community, its social ambiance
(involving close family and social ties among residents, staff and
community members), and its psychological significance for the

community as "our" nursing home. He argues that the permeability of such a facility, reflected in the constant flow of people between the facility and the community and the blurring of the boundary between "inside" and "outside," results in a long-term care institution that is a part of the community rather than separated from it. Rowles suggests that this naturally occurring interdependent relationship can form the basis of an expanded role for the rural nursing home. Specifically, he suggests the potential for such facilities to provide the focus of an expanded array of functions including serving as bases for home care programs, sites for adult day care, and the locus of assisted-living housing options in campus settings. Such multifunctional complexes may become significant in rural economic development as well as health care, particularly if Rowles is correct in his hypothesis that quasi-familial care is more likely to be provided in rural than in urban facilities.

An expanded role as a provider of long-term care is also suggested by Schlenker and Shaughnessy in their chapter exploring the role of rural hospitals in long-term care (Chapter 7). Rural hospitals, in response to major fiscal constraints that resulted from introduction of the prospective payment system (PPS), are gradually moving into long-term care. This movement has a number of manifestations including the introduction of swing-beds and the development of on-site long-term care units or closely affiliated nursing homes.

Chapter 3 through Chapter 7 paint a picture of a highly fragmented and incomplete system of long-term care in most rural areas. Each of the authors reaffirms the need for major reorientation and reorganization of long-term care programs and services in rural areas. In particular, there is a need for fiscal reform that will enhance the potential for achieving equal access to needed services. It would have been appropriate to complement the diagnosis with a discussion of pending remedies. However, as is now well known, the national debate on health care reform that dominated the 103rd Congress resulted in a stalemate and inaction. While a number of states have begun to develop health care reform initiatives with potential implications for rural long-term care, change on the national level is unlikely within the current political climate.

Andrew Coburn (Chapter 8) provides an important commentary in his discussion of the implications of the failed national health care reform movement for rural long-term care. He notes that rural health care providers are "not waiting for national reform to transform themselves into new organizational and financial structures that can survive in an increasingly competitive health care market place" (p. 157). In the face of such private sector initiatives, Coburn argues that it will become increasingly important for rural long-term care consumers to make themselves heard in what has become a highly volatile policy arena.

Some aspects of such involvement and assumption of responsibility by rural elders and their families are incorporated in a concluding chapter, which attempts to integrate many of the themes in this book. Beaulieu, Rowles, and Myers (Chapter 9) present a set of guiding principles for the development of rural long-term care systems that are both comprehensive and at the same time sensitive to the realities of rural America. First, we argue for local community control of rural long-term care systems; adoption of nonlinear models of care (in preference to the "continuum of care" philosophy with which the nation seems to be enamored); a client-centered philosophy of care; family-centered decision making, centralized access to information, enhanced cooperation among providers, and redefinition of health care professional roles and training in ways that enrich the personnel resource base of rural areas. In our synthesis of these principles, we seek to present a vision of the future that can guide the development of rural long-term care into the next century.

Although this volume considers a wide array of perspectives and each contributor adds his or her own particular nuance to consideration of the problem, several recurring themes emerge. Many elders and their families are currently experiencing the historical legacy of a haphazardly developed system of long-term care in much of rural America. Our contributors are united in their indictment of this system as it has evolved into a fragmentary and uncoordinated array of options that, in many communities, denies access to needed programs and services.

Second, our contributors consistently reiterate the theme of regional and local variation. As Magilvy (Chapter 4) reminds us, variation within rural areas is often greater than that between rural and urban areas. Both regional differences in the characteristics and resources of rural areas and differences among rural elderly populations with respect to demography, economic circumstances, life histories and culture, are such that it is unreasonable to expect and inappropriate to seek a universally applicable long-term care system in rural America.

A third recurrent theme is the seemingly obligatory call for more research. In this case, the call is far more than the academic's customary call for more information. Rather it is symptomatic of the magnitude of our ignorance regarding the way in which elderly people in rural America and their families cope with increasing frailty. As will become apparent in the pages that follow, we lack basic information on crucial topics ranging from the availability and accessibility of services, through understanding of the way in which informal support systems operate in rural areas, to key aspects of rural long-term care administration and financing.

Acknowledging the paucity of basic research from which to draw inferences, several of our contributors are nonetheless able to identify key characteristics of long-term care in rural areas. For example, a consistent theme is the greater role of informal support in rural than in urban areas (see Stoller, Chapter 3, and Magilvy, Chapter 4). This trait may be part of the explanation for the more informal ambiance and culture and high level of community integration of rural nursing homes that Rowles posits in Chapter 6. Indeed, several chapters contribute insight into the distinctive meaning of caregiving and its relationship to the provision of long-term care in rural areas.

Insights which point to the distinctiveness of the rural context provide further reinforcement for what has become almost a platitude: It is inappropriate to transport scaled-down versions of urban programs to rural areas. Additional ammunition for this argument is provided by most of the contributors to this collection as they describe new programs and emergent themes in long-term care that have significant implications for the way in which we can anticipate the rural long-term care system to develop over the next few years. For example, growing concern with developing options for subacute care is resulting in the emergence of "short-term long-term care," a trend that has the potential to transform the roles of both rural hospitals and rural nursing homes. Home health care has an increasingly important role in long-term care and is an area of rapid innovation.

Our society harbors the opinion that rural health care is of lower quality than the care available in large cities. Notably absent from the recurring lists of problems presented in the literature and discussed at the Lexington conference are concerns regarding the quality of particular elements of rural long-term care. Indeed, Rowles (Chapter 6) suggests that rural nursing homes may have some advantages over their urban counterparts.

A constant underlying theme in the quest for new solutions is a concern with issues of reimbursement and long-term care financing. Coburn (Chapter 8) argues that an obsession with financing at the expense of programmatic content has diverted attention from key issues of substance and consideration of the design of appropriate rural long-term care systems. Clearly, issues of reimbursement are important. For example, as Schlenker and Shaughnessy (Chapter 7) point out, there is a need for an integrated long-term care payment system that does not include incentives for inappropriate transfers, for example, relocating an older person based on a change in program eligibility rather than an alteration in health status. However, as several of our contributors point out, it is important to consider what we want out of a long-term care system and what underlying philosophy we want this system to reflect. The finance theme can be reduced to a question of values and the level and type of support we are prepared to provide for our elders.

Ultimately, as several contributors note (Coward et al., Magilvy, and Coburn), the future of long-term care in rural America will be decided in the political arena. Currently, the politics of avoidance appear to be ascendent. As powerful lobby groups reinforce the status quo, the problem of developing fiscally viable, integrated, comprehensive, and community-sensitive systems of rural long-term care is relegated to the back burner of national consciousness.

Presently, there appears to be a lack of either a vision of the possible or a national will to address this admittedly complex issue. In the meantime, significant numbers of rural elders and their families continue to suffer the consequences of inadequate long-term care.

In the pages that follow we seek to provide a diagnosis of the problem and some potential remedies that might serve to ignite debate on the future of rural long-term care. If we can encourage scholars, planners, and policymakers, as well as rural community residents, to take up the challenge of critically examining the future of rural long-term care and moving toward a shared vision of the future, then we shall have accomplished a primary objective of this endeavor.

REFERENCES

Kane, R. A., & Kane, R. L. (1987). *Long-term care: Principles, programs and policies.* New York: Springer Publishing Co.

Rowles, G. D., Beaulieu, J. E., & Myers, W. W. (1994). *Contemporary directions in long-term care for the rural elderly.* Position statement based on September 1994 Conference, Lexington, KY: Sanders-Brown Center on Aging.

Obstacles to Creating High-Quality Long-Term Care Services for Rural Elders

2

Raymond T. Coward
Julie K. Netzer
Chuck W. Peek

The primary goal of this chapter is to describe and discuss six obstacles that inhibit the efforts of concerned citizens, service providers, advocates, and public officials who are committed to providing high-quality long-term care services to needy older adults regardless of their place of residence. At one level, the public policy goal of "equal access" has always been relatively simple and straightforward to articulate, although bewilderingly elusive to achieve. As its most basic premise, this policy goal includes a commitment to accord individuals access to publicly financed services regardless of who they are or where they live. In theory, therefore, older Americans should have access to a basic set of services wherever they choose to live (a variant of the so-called safety net). Unfortunately, the reality is that equal access has not been uniformly accomplished for certain subgroups of the aging population. A combination of political circumstances and finite resources has constrained the availability of critically important services.

The consequence of our failure to consistently implement this goal, given the focus of this book, is that, in general, older adults who live in sparsely populated and remote rural settings have access to a smaller number and narrower range of long-term care services compared to their age counterparts who live in more urban and suburban settings (Coward, Bull, Kukulka, & Galliher, 1994).[1]

There are, certainly, exceptions to this trend in terms of both services and places. For example, certain long-term care services, like nursing home beds, appear to be more abundant (as judged by the number of nursing home beds per 1,000 elders) in nonmetropolitan counties than they are in metropolitan counties (Coward, Duncan, & Uttaro, 1996; Shaughnessy, 1994). Similarly, some rural communities are known to have well-developed systems of long-term care for their elderly residents, with a wide variety of in-home, community-based, and institutional services (Coward & Dwyer, 1991). But these are exceptions, not the rule, and should not divert our attention from what, for the vast majority of older rural Americans, is a basic fact of life: There are fewer formal services available to them, and their families, as they cope with their need for long-term care.

The lesser availability of rural services does not appear to be based on less need for such services among rural elders. Although we may quibble over the precise magnitude of residential differences in health (Leinbach, 1988), there is substantial evidence suggesting that many rural elders have an equal or greater need for services than their more urban and suburban counterparts (Coward, Vogel, Duncan, & Uttaro, 1995; Cutler & Coward, 1988; Dwyer, Lee, & Coward, 1990; Lassey & Lassey, 1985; Lee & Lassey, 1980; U.S. Senate Special Committee on Aging, 1992). Some of this disadvantage is due to the increased vulnerability of residing in rural America in general (Jensen, 1991; Rowland & Lyons, 1989); whereas other dimensions are a result of the "triple jeopardy" of older populations (Coward & Dwyer, 1991)—that is, the consequences of the combination of growing older, residing in a sparsely populated and remote rural setting, and contending with the greater prevalence of certain sociodemographic conditions that negatively affect health. Thus, in addition to coping with the declining health and increasing physical limitations that generally accompany aging, the lives of elders in rural areas are further complicated by the lack of formal services, greater distances to travel, less public transportation and other logistical circumstances that complicate the lives of older people in these settings. Further, specific risk factors associated with poor health—such as low income, poor and dilapidated housing, lower levels of education, and higher rates of alcohol and cigarette consumption—are more pervasive in older rural populations than they are in urban or suburban populations of the elderly.[2] The combination of these circumstances has led some health analysts to suggest that rural elders may be a particularly at-risk and vulnerable group (Greene, 1984; Krout, 1986; Sharp, Halpert, & Breytspraak, 1988). Even if one accepts the argument that the magnitude of the residential differences may be statistically significant but not of programmatic significance (Leinbach, 1988), the same level of need confronted in a milieu of fewer supportive services is still a reason for concern (Coward & Cutler, 1989). This raises questions about whether elders are at greater risk of poor health outcomes as a consequence of their place of residence.

Faced with the widespread reality of fewer services in rural areas, the question that often troubles health advocates is: Why don't we have a first-class system of long-term care services in rural America? That is, what is stopping us from implementing a system of long-term care services in rural America that we think is appropriate and adequate? In a broad sense, this entire book attempts to shed light on these questions. The other chapters in this volume describe and discuss the difficulties and complexities faced by health care workers as they deliver specific long-term care services in rural environments. In contrast, our purpose in this chapter is to step back from the "nuts and bolts" problems of service delivery in rural areas and to identify some of the overarching challenges that face rural service providers and planners.

THE CHALLENGE

Six major obstacles inhibit our attempts to develop better long-term care for rural elders. These, of course, are not an exhaustive list of the difficulties we face in creating and delivering high-quality long-term care services to elders in rural America. They are, however, a starting point for a dialogue and debate about the obstacles that must be overcome. The six obstacles are:

1. Lack of a clear consensus among consumers, care providers, and social policy analysts about what a basic rural long-term care system should contain and how it should be organized

2. The difficulty of attracting and retaining professional personnel needed to staff long-term care services in rural areas

3. Problems of molding diverse and multifaceted types of long-term care services into a coordinated and coherent whole

4. The dearth of models of long-term care that reflect both the needs and the characteristics of rural communities

5. The question of how to pay for long-term care services, especially rural long-term care, which in some places costs more to deliver than its urban counterparts

6. The lack of empirical data about rural elders, their quality of life, their needs and circumstances, and the effectiveness of existing programs and organizations that deliver services to this population

In the sections that follow, we elaborate on each of these issues, highlighting in more detail the precise problems associated with each obstacle, and where possible, offering general suggestions as to how we can meet these challenges.

The Lack of a Consensus

Because there are widely divergent opinions among consumers, providers, and health planners about what services are essential to maintaining elders in the least restrictive environment, there is a lack of a consensus on what a rural long-term care system should contain and how it should be organized. We do not mean to imply that a single system, or a universal way of doing things, can be created and applied to the wide range and variety of rural contexts that exist in America. Rural communities are not "cookie-cutter" replicas of each other and, therefore, they need the flexibility to create a system of care that reflects their unique environments. We do maintain, however, that it is essential that there be a shared vision of the ultimate direction toward which rural long-term care should be moving. Specifically, we need to reach agreement on which long-term care services should be available to all older Americans regardless of where they live.

Some gerontologists have promoted a *continuum of care* as the ultimate vision of a long-term care system for elders as they cope with their changing health status and physical abilities. Proponents of this kind of system envision the availability of a wide variety of health and human services that reflect decreasing levels of independence among elders and increasing needs for support by others. On the one end of the continuum are services that support healthy, ambulatory elders living independently in the community. Such services as senior centers, information and referral services, and job-search and training programs provide support to older adults who are quite healthy and able to care for themselves. As disabilities increase, and mobility declines, services further along on the continuum are designed to assist more frail and disabled elders. Services like home-delivered meals, home health nurses and adult day care are intended to provide support and assistance to a more impaired older population. At the far extreme of the continuum are skilled nursing care facilities equipped to offer 24-hour nursing care and to treat the more severe medical conditions of older persons.

By having such a continuum of care available, service planners hope to create a community setting that is better able to respond to the changing needs of older adults as they age. But is it feasible to think that we can recreate such a system in every small town and rural village in the United States? Is this a realistic goal toward which we should all be working? Some rural gerontologists do not think so. Indeed, Coward and Cutler (1988) have argued that the concept of a continuum of care is far too resource intensive to be a reasonable alternative for most rural communities and should not be the vision that guides our efforts to improve rural long-term care systems.

Alternatively, other rural health analysts have recommended that we identify a basic set of services and work toward making those services universally available (Coward, 1992). To identify such a "basic package" of services will require dialogue and debate among providers, consumers, and health planners that is directed at reaching agreement over what services are essential to ensuring a basic quality of life for older persons. Alaska has made some progress toward this goal (Coward, Duncan, & Netzer, 1993). Under the provisions of the Older Alaskans Plan, each community in the state is evaluated on the size of its population, the organization of its government, its accessibility and proximity to a larger city, and the transportation and communications infrastructure that it has built. As a result of this assessment, each community is placed into one of five service tiers. Each successive tier represents the availability of a wider and more diverse set of health and human services for elders. Thus, certain basic services are available to older persons regardless of the type of community in which they live, whereas other more advanced services are only available in nearby communities. It is this kind of thoughtful, organized, and planned system of service location that some rural health analysts believe is the only way that we can achieve an equitable distribution of resources (Leonfanti & Chiesa, 1988). Although regional planning for health services is no longer in vogue, without such strategic development the evolution of our system of long-term care in the United States may continue to be haphazard and uneven.

It is not our purpose in this chapter to urge the adoption of one particular vision of an ideal system over another. Rather, our point is to remind readers that without a clear vision of where we are going, it is unlikely that we will be able to achieve the fair distribution of services that we seek. The consequences of continuing in our current mode of operation will be the perpetuation of an extremely uneven set of circumstances for rural elders. Some rural elders live in locations where they have access to a wide range and variety of services, providing them with options that enhance their quality of life and prolong their ability to live independently. Unfortunately, other rural elders live in communities that offer them virtually no formal support or services to aid them as they cope with declining health and increasing physical limitations. To reduce or eradicate these disparities will require some shared vision of the ultimate system that we are trying to create. At present, one does not exist.

Health Services Personnel

The second major obstacle to achieving more widely dispersed long-term care services for rural elders is the inability of small towns and rural communities to attract and retain an adequate work force of health care providers. Although about one in four older Americans lives in a small town or rural area, the proportion of health care professionals that practice in such places is even smaller. For example, in 1986, nonmetropolitan counties had 44% fewer physicians (MDs and ODs) per capita than did their metropolitan counterparts (Hicks, 1990). This pattern is pervasive across the full spectrum of health care professions: Disproportionately fewer nurses, social workers, dentists, physical therapists, psychologists, lab technicians, X-ray technicians, and opticians practice in rural areas (Gesler & Ricketts, 1992; Wright & Jablonowski, 1987). Very small rural communities (those with populations under 1,000) have a particularly difficult time attracting and retaining health care providers (Movassaghi & Kindig, 1989).

Although we do not have a complete understanding of all the dimensions that contribute to the difficulties of recruiting and retaining health care providers in sparsely populated and remote rural settings, we do have some ideas about how to overcome the maldistributions and have witnessed some states achieve remarkable success in altering existing patterns of locational choice (Bruce & Norton, 1984). For example, Crandall, Dwyer, and Duncan (1990) have identified two general approaches to improving the availability of health care professionals in rural areas: the economic incentive model and the indenture model. The economic incentive model provides incentives for providers (such as salary supplements, income guarantees, and fee augmentations) for practicing in a rural area. In contrast, the indenture approach provides students with educational loans in exchange for later service in underserved areas, such as rural communities.

Coward, Duncan, and Netzer (1993) have argued that states can take actions to improve the distribution of providers, given the substantial support they provide to higher education programs in the health professions. For example, states can make loans available to attend state-supported health professional schools that would be repaid by student recipients through service in underserved rural areas (as is currently being proposed in Vermont). Or, state legislators might tie the level of funding of a state-supported health professions program to the number or proportion of its graduates who ultimately become employed in a rural environment within the state. Unfortunately, although a number of successful techniques for altering the locational choices of health care providers have been identified over the past two decades (Fickenscher, 1992), they are too rarely implemented to make a significant difference from a national perspective.

Other attempts to cope with an inadequate supply of health care providers have focused on innovative strategies for delivering care in sparsely populated and remote places. For example, Wallace and Colsher (1994) have highlighted some innovative attempts to bring acute care services to elders in rural America. Some of these include the use of telecommunication systems which link urban-based medical centers with rural health care providers for diagnosis, treatment, and related consultations. Another innovative strategy is the use of periodic visits, mobile units, or clinics staffed by outreach physicians and other health care professionals that are intended to augment locally available care in rural areas with specialized services oriented toward the older adult (Wallace & Colsher, 1994).

Although technologically oriented strategies hold great promise, "virtual care" should not be viewed as a panacea for the difficulties involved in providing medical services to elders living in rural areas. The development and implementation of technological innovations that facilitate the diagnosis and treatment of patients in remote locations are subject to some of the same obstacles that face more traditional methods of care delivery. For example, consensus must be reached regarding which services to provide and where to provide them. A more vexing issue involves funding: What sources will provide the financial resources necessary to develop and maintain these costly systems?

At the same time that communities have been seeking innovative ways to attract and retain rural health care providers, or to supplement locally offered services with specialized services, others have urged the commitment of resources to train existing rural health providers in the care of older adults. In some states, for example, federally sponsored geriatric education centers (GECs) are conducting educational and training programs in rural gerontology. Rural practitioners may have difficulty in leaving their locations for additional training and continuing education; thus, mailed educational materials, teleconferencing, and the use of computerized information searches are all solutions that may assist rural practitioners in providing state-of-the-art health care (Wallace & Colsher, 1994).

In the end, we seem to have available to us a number of different ways to address and correct many of the problems associated with creating a professional work force that is both knowledgeable about, and dedicated to, rural long-term care and service delivery. What we may lack is the political will, or the political consciousness, to sustain the effort that it will take to reverse the trend of professionals being trained in urban-based settings and, ultimately, practicing in urban communities. Therefore, we must continue, as rural advocates, to educate our political leaders about the human, social, and financial costs of an inadequate long-term care system for rural Americans. Unless we do this, it will continue to be difficult, if not impossible, to engender the political support necessary to improve the quality of life for those rural elders in need of long-term care.

The Coordination of Services

The third challenge we face is creating and developing a coordinated, cohesive, and effective system of long-term care services for rural elders. The phrase *long-term care* was once used almost exclusively as a synonym for admission into a nursing home. Today, it is used much more broadly to refer to a wide range of activities and services that address the needs of persons with chronic illness or physical disabilities. In this larger context, informal family care, community-based services, in-home care, as well as services delivered to elders living in a variety of different housing alternatives (including nursing homes) are all incorporated under the rubric of long-term care. Most of the chapters in this book discuss one of these important components of rural long-term care.

As it exists currently, the long-term care "system" that older adults and their families must navigate has been described as an uncoordinated and fragmented collection of often competing services (Coward, Duncan, & Netzer, 1993). The result is a collection of entities, some well defined and bounded, others loosely connected and constantly shifting, but all operating with different motives, pursuing different agendas, and functioning with various levels of efficiency and effectiveness. Some elements of the system are private, proprietary enterprises, whereas other parts are public entities. The very foundation of the system, however, is found neither in the private nor public sector, but is informal in nature. (See Chapter 3 in this volume by Eleanor Palo Stoller on the role of the family in rural long-term care.) A vast network of aid and assistance is built on family and blood ties, feelings of filial responsibility, personal affection, and mutual obligation (Dwyer & Coward, 1992; Hamon & Bliezsner, 1990; Stoller, 1983; Stone, Cafferata, & Sangl, 1987).

The one property of a true system that the current circumstances do reflect is the interconnectedness of the parts; that is, changes that affect any part of the system have consequences—both intended and unintended—for the other components. For example, the implementation of diagnosis-related groups (DRGs) by hospitals has resulted in increased numbers of families and home health agencies caring for elders who are discharged from hospitals "sicker and quicker" (Glazer, 1990). It is similarly true that advances in medical technology, combined with the rapid growth of the home health industry in the 1980s, has altered the flow of admissions into nursing homes (Rivlin, Wiener, Hanley, & Spence, 1988). In today's health care environment, nursing homes are much more apt to be asked to care for older persons with greater acuteness of illness, requiring skilled nursing care of a greater intensity (Shaughnessy, 1994).

It has been argued that the fragmentation of the long-term care system that results from uneven coverage and haphazard development is a greater problem for rural elders than it is for their urban or suburban counterparts (Coward & Rathbone-McCuan, 1985). For urban elders and their families, the frustration and confusion of navigating the maze of agencies and regulations that comprise our long-term care system is both real and undeniable. Yet, for those who persist, there is often a reward at the other end; that is, services that can be of assistance. Most urban and suburban places in the United States, unlike most rural areas, have a substantial range of services available to older adults and their families (Coward, Bull, Kukulka, & Galliher, 1994; Coward & Cutler, 1989; Coward et al., 1993; Krout, 1986; Nelson, 1983). Some may have waiting lists, others may be inconveniently located, and still others may be expensive; but, in the end, they are there. This is seldom the case in rural America (Coward, Bull, et al., 1994). As we mentioned earlier in this chapter, in most parts of the rural United States there are far fewer services available, in terms of both sheer numbers and types of services. Indeed, services designed to assist the most frail and disabled elderly (such as adult day care services, assisted-living facilities, skilled Medicare home health services, or visiting nurses) are severely lacking in rural areas (Krout, 1994; Nelson, 1980, 1983, 1994; Taietz & Milton, 1979).

The result of this uneven distribution of services is an increased reliance on family members to care for more disabled elders in sparsely populated and remote rural areas (Lee, Dwyer, & Coward, 1990; Mercier, Paulson, & Morris, 1988). For example, Coward, Cutler, and Mullens (1990), using data from the National Health Interview Survey, have shown that severely disabled elders (i.e., elders experiencing difficulties performing nine or more activities of daily living [ADL] or instrumental activities of daily living [IADL] tasks) are less likely than their urban or suburban counterparts to be receiving aid from a formal service provider and are significantly more likely to be receiving aid exclusively from informal helpers. That is, nearly half (42.7%) of severely disabled elders who lived in large central cities reported receiving formal services. Among those elders living in metropolitan places outside central cities (sometimes referred to as the suburbs), the proportion receiving formal services was 39.6%. However, among elders living in nonmetropolitan places, only about one in four (26.3%) reported receiving formal service assistance. Simultaneously, there were significant residential differences in the percentage of older adults who relied exclusively on informal sources for their care. Specifically, 55.2% of older central city residents, and 59.0% of older metropolitan residents living outside central cities, relied exclusively on informal sources of care for their assistance. In contrast, nearly three of four (73.0%) severely disabled nonmetropolitan residents relied exclusively on informal sources of care.

Thus, the unsystematic and uncoordinated way that we have allowed our system of long-term care services to develop in the United States has resulted in significant service gaps in many rural communities. As a consequence, rural elders are often forced to make choices based on a more limited array of formal service options than those available to their more urban and suburban counterparts. For example, Coward, Duncan, and Freudenberger (1994) recently reported on interviews that were conducted with newly admitted elders in a set of both rural and urban nursing homes. The results indicated that new residents who had lived in rural communities were more apt to answer yes to the question: "Were there any services you needed before you entered the nursing home that were not available in the community where you lived?" Nearly half (47.3%) of the new admissions from rural areas reported that needed services were not available to them, compared to one in four newly admitted elders in urban nursing homes. Even when a logistic regression model was estimated that included the age of the respondent and the difficulties they reported performing ADLs and IADLs (the three variables on which there had been statistical differences between the two residential groups), rural elders were still 2.68 times more likely to report that they had needed services that were unavailable. The authors speculated that this finding may have been the result of (a) unfamiliarity, on the part of rural elders, with the formal health and human services system in their area; (b) a mismatch between the needs of the elders and the eligibility and reimbursement criteria for community-based services; or (c) a lack of appreciation among certain providers of the viability of home care as a health care option. Whatever the cause, the fact remains that most rural elders make choices about their long-term care within a context that is distinctly different than their counterparts who reside in more urban and suburban places.

It is our judgment that in order to achieve a truly first-class system of long-term care services for rural elders, it will be necessary to create public policy mechanisms that better coordinate, manage, and control the many and varied elements that now comprise the long-term care system in our country. Without the ability and authority to coordinate the various parts of this system, we fear that rural communities (and, ultimately, the older adults and their families who live there) will continue to be at the mercy of an organizational hydra that is fed by the individual motivations, demands, and visions of an unrelated set of public agencies and private corporations. These are the circumstances under which we currently operate; and we know that they have not served many rural elders well. As a consequence, we must seek more effective ways of molding the disparate parts that now comprise the system into a coordinated whole.

Rural Models

The fourth barrier we face in attempts to construct a better system of long-term care services for rural elders is a lack of truly rural models for delivering such services. Rural service delivery models need to evolve from and reflect the distinctive life circumstances of rural elders and build on the best of what rural communities have to offer their residents. Conversely, residents of rural communities may have needs that are not anticipated by urban models of care. Coward and Rathbone-McCuan (1985) have argued that rural communities and rural elders need to be recognized not only for their similarities to their urban counterparts, but also for their differences from urban and suburban environments and their elderly populations. As these authors, and others (Krout, 1994; Longino & Smith, 1994), have argued, it is essential that the service delivery systems implemented in rural areas not be simply watered-down variants of urban models, but ones that embody the unique needs and distinctive life circumstances of rural elders and the environments in which they live.

In the past we were hampered by the fact that there was very little money available to support the development of rurally oriented service innovations. While not perfect, the situation today has improved dramatically. For example, the federal Office of Rural Health Policy of the Health Resources and Services Administration funds dozens of innovative demonstration programs designed to improve the rural health system. In addition, there are several major private philanthropic organizations, such as the Robert Wood Johnson Foundation, the W. K. Kellogg Foundation, and the Ford Foundation, that have traditions of seeking new and better ways of serving America's rural populations. On the research side, the Agency for Health Care Policy and Research (AHCPR), the National Institute on Aging, the National Institute for Nursing Research, and the National Institute for Mental Health, have all recently funded innovative research and demonstration projects aimed at addressing the needs of disabled, frail, and vulnerable older rural Americans.

Although each of these research and demonstration initiatives has been enormously useful in improving rural circumstances, one significant challenge continues to inhibit our ability to achieve widespread improvements: We have an inadequate mechanism for disseminating information about successful rural long-term care programs. There are successful models for delivering long-term care services alive and well and functioning in rural America; unfortunately, few people know about them. They are like well-kept secrets and, as a consequence, rural service providers spend an inordinate amount of time reinventing the wheel. Perhaps this situation will soon change. Recently, the Administration on Aging

(AoA) created a National Resource Center on Rural Long-Term Care at the University of Kansas Medical Center.[3] Part of the mandate of that center is to identify innovative rural long-term care programs and disseminate information about their operations and outcomes to other providers.

Still, if major transformations in our system of rural long-term care services are to occur, what is needed is a routinized method for getting information about successful programs into the hands of rural providers, planners, public officials, and private individuals who are seeking solutions to the long-term care problems they face in their communities. Without such a mechanism, too many of our operational, personnel, and psychic resources will be spent repeating the errors of others and failing to capitalize on the successes of rural colleagues. Likewise, information about successful rural programs can inform research and development that is aimed at creating more effective and comprehensive rural models.

Financing Rural Long-Term Care

The fifth obstacle to creating an effective rural long-term care system may be the most difficult and contentious to resolve; that is, how to pay for it. In the United States, unlike certain other developed countries, we have not reached a consensus on how to pay for the long-term care of frail and disabled older adults (Rivlin et al., 1988). Undoubtedly, many practitioners involved in the delivery of long-term care services have faced the dilemma in recent years of a rising demand for their services, at a time when their budgets are declining, not rising, or rising at a rate that does not keep pace with inflation. Today, many long-term care programs are operating with client waiting lists because there simply are not enough resources to serve everyone in need of help. Other providers are forced to make daily decisions about who will be served and how they will be served based on the realities of their budgets and the complex financing systems within which they operate. Decisions about who gets what services are often based on reimbursement policies—and the fit between the needs of clients and reimbursement mechanisms is not always perfect. Many rural advocates believe that the lack of flexibility in currently existing reimburse-ment systems decreases the ability of service providers to respond adequately to the needs of the elders they purport to serve (Coward, Bull, et al., 1994). Tailoring reimbursement mechanisms to meet the specific needs of rural elders is one of the key issues that must be addressed by the rural models of care discussed in the previous section.

It is also interesting to note that the debate over health care reform that occurred throughout 1994 included very little dialogue or discussion about how to finance long-term care services. Few of the plans and proposals presented to Congress that year included any mention of long-term care and those that did offered limits on such care (Blendon, Brodie, & Benson, 1995; Lundberg, 1994). The absence of attention to this issue is certainly not attributable to an adequate system for financing long-term care or to older people's unconcern about the expense of long-term care. Nor is it because long-term care represents an insignificant portion of our overall health care expenditures. The question is not whether long-term care costs will rise, but, rather, how these increases will be distrib-uted between private (i.e., individuals, families, and private long-term care insurance) and public (i.e., government financing and entitlements, taxes, and public insurance) sources of revenues (Rivlin et al., 1988).

It is unlikely that the problem of financing long-term care will soon be resolved. There just does not seem to be the political will to address this very difficult issue. First, it would probably require a substantial investment of new resources to build a truly first-class system of long-term care in the United States. Given the dif-ficulties that persist in our economy, and the proportion of our gross national product that we already spend on health care, it is unlikely that public policymakers will decide to increase spending in this arena. If anything, the mood of the country seems to be toward finding ways of reducing our expenditures on health care. As a consequence, debates over the expansion of services often dis-solve into battles between existing service sectors. (For example, the expansion of home health care is frequently pitted against the huge resources that we currently spend on institutionalized care.)

Second, there is no clear consensus in our nation about who should be responsible for the long-term care needs of our elderly residents. Thus, once again, we have a division of opinion that makes it politically risky for some politicians to step forward and lead our nation to a solution of these problems, they seem to be waiting for the winds of opinion to blow in one direction or another. Exacerbating inaction on the part of politicians is the influence of some powerful lobbies that, because of self-interests, oppose radical changes in the current system no matter how poorly it serves certain subgroups (such as rural elders). Finally, there does not seem to be much political determination to address any national problems that are unquestionably complex and difficult, as identifying a method for financing long-term care over the next two decades clearly is. We do not mean to be pessimists about these financing problems, but, frankly, given the political and economic realities of the United States in the mid-1990s, it is difficult to be anything but doubtful about achieving any significant breakthroughs. On the other hand, the aging of the U.S. population, especially the graying of the baby boom cohort, may exert sufficient social and economic force to create a political environment conducive to change. To capitalize on these opportunities, however, will require informal dialogue and coordinated efforts on the part of service providers, advocates, and researchers.

Research

The last piece in the puzzle of quality long-term care for rural America is the need for more research. Efforts to create a better system of long-term care services for elders who live in small towns and rural communities are hampered by a lack of information that would lead to better understanding of the consequences of poor health, fewer services, and lesser accessibility to existing services for the quality of life of rural older adults (Coward, Bull, et al., 1994).

Indeed, our ability to address the five preceding obstacles, our ability to characterize fully the unique circumstances and needs of people who grow old in sparsely populated and remote rural communities, and our ability to identify effective and efficient rural health service delivery systems are each, to some degree, diminished by a lack of data. Acquiring the missing information is not something that should divide researchers and practitioners (i.e., money directed toward research should not be seen by providers as diverting resources from their efforts). Rather, what is needed is a partnership between service providers and researchers so that they can work cooperatively and collaboratively toward creating the firm empirical base of knowledge that is essential to addressing the challenges we face.

Although others have chronicled the specific research questions that are of highest priority with regard to rural long-term care services,[4] we would like to emphasize several important overarching lines of inquiry that, in our judgment, require immediate increased attention:

- We need a better understanding of the consequences of the lesser availability of long-term care services in rural areas. We need to know the effects of these deficiencies on the health and quality of life of elders and their families and the ultimate effect of deficient long-term care on overall expenditures in the health care system.

- We need a better understanding of which long-term care service strategies and mechanisms are effective, and which are not, in sparsely populated and remote rural settings. Moreover, proposed research needs to be conducted in a manner that permits us to identify the underlying mechanisms or principles that characterize successful interventions.

- We need better data on the costs of different rural services and their comparative impact on the long-term needs of rural elders and the quality of their lives. That is, we need to understand the relative returns from investments in certain types of services.

- We need ongoing and systematic programs of research that assess the effectiveness and efficiency of systems that are designed to link rural and urban providers in order to serve the needs of geographically isolated populations and reduce the fragmentation that currently exists. We also need more research that evaluates innovative methods for coordinating long-term care services in rural areas.

- Finally, we need more research on the impact and effectiveness of employing a variety of alternative service providers (e.g., nurse practitioners, physician assistants, specially trained paramedics) in meeting the long-term care needs of older rural residents.

SUMMARY

Evidence suggests that the need for long-term care among older persons who live in sparsely populated and remote rural communities is equal to or greater than among their age counterparts who live in more urban and suburban settings. Simultaneously, there is ample evidence to suggest that older adults who live in sparsely populated and remote rural settings tend to have access to a smaller number and narrower range of long-term care services than their contemporaries who live in other residential contexts. In this chapter we have reviewed six obstacles that are inhibiting our ability to create high-quality long-term care services for rural elders. Although this list is by no means exhaustive, it begins to identify major barriers that are obstructing our quest for equality access to services for all elders, regardless of where they live. Collectively, these barriers provide a general framework within which we can examine and consider the specific difficulties and complexities (described and elaborated in subsequent chapters of this book) that confront service providers who are dedicated to improving long-term care services for rural elders.

ACKNOWLEDGMENTS

The preparation of this chapter was supported, in part, by grants from the National Institute on Aging (AG09649) and the Agency for Health Care Policy and Research (HS00088 and HS00086). The opinions expressed here, however, are those of the authors and do not, necessarily, reflect those of the funding agencies. Requests for further information should be sent to: Raymond T. Coward, Director, Center on Rural Health and Aging, J. Hillis Miller Health Science Center, The University of Florida, P. O. Box 100177, Gainesville, FL 32610–0177.

NOTES

1. Throughout this chapter, we use the terms *rural* and *urban* in generic ways rather than only when they conform to the strict U.S. Census definitions for these terms. Moreover, we use the terms *rural* and *nonmetropolitan,* and *urban* and *metropolitan,* interchangeably—although we are aware of their different definitions (see Hewitt, 1989, for a detailed discussion of the various definitions that have been used to describe rural areas). We conceptualize residence as a continuum (see Coward & Cutler, 1988, for a further discussion of this concept). At one end of the continuum are very large cities, such as New York, Chicago, and Miami. At the other end of the continuum are the very small and remote places, like Lake Moxie, Maine, Hebron, Mississippi, and North Fork, Idaho. For the most part, when we refer to rural places in the United States, we have in mind settings that are both sparsely populated and physically removed from a large urban setting. When we refer to findings from a specific study, however, we will attempt to use the residence categories employed by the original investigators.

2. There are a number of excellent reviews of the literature that describe residential differences in the prevalence of certain factors that appear to put older adults at risk of poor health outcomes. For example, see McLaughlin and Jensen (1993) for a comparison of income and poverty levels and Clark (1992) for contrasts in housing stock. Bainton (1981) offers a review of residential differences in substance abuse among elders and the U.S. Senate Special Committee on Aging (1992) has released comparisons of educational levels.

3. For further information about this center and its activities, write: Dr. Linda J. Redford, Director, National Resource Center on Rural Long-Term Care, University of Kansas Medical Center, Room 5026 Wescoe Pavilion, Kansas City, Kansas, 66160–7117.

4. A recent volume that emerged from a national conference sponsored by the Robert Wood Johnson Foundation and the W. K. Kellogg Foundation offers an "action agenda" that describes endeavors that should be taken to improve the

long-term care of older persons living in small towns and rural communities (Coward, Bull, et al., 1994). The conference identified critical actions in three basic areas, producing an agenda for research and scholarly pursuits, an agenda for health policy and legislative actions, and an agenda for program and services development. In particular, see the chapters in that volume on informal care networks (Stoller & Lee, 1994), in-home services (Nelson, 1994), community-based services (Krout, 1994), ambulatory and acute care services (Wallace & Colsher, 1994), and institutionalized care (Shaughnessy, 1994).

REFERENCES

Bainton, B. (1981). Drinking patterns of the rural aged. In C. L. Fry (Ed.), *Dimensions: Aging, culture and health* (pp. 55–76). New York: Bergin.

Blendon, R. J., Brodie, M., & Benson, J. (1995). What should be done now that national health system reform is dead? *Journal of the American Medical Association, 273*, 243–244.

Bruce, T. A., & Norton, W. R. (1984). *Improving rural health: Initiatives of an academic medical center.* Little Rock, AR: Rose.

Clark, B. S. (1992). Housing for rural elders. In C. N. Bull & S. D. Bane (Eds.), *The future of aging in rural America* (pp. 101–105). Kansas City, MO: National Resource Center for Rural Elderly.

Coward, R. T. (1992). Improving health care for rural elders: What do we know? What can we do? In C. N. Bull & S. D. Bane (Eds.), *The future of aging in rural America* (pp. 37–50). Kansas City, MO: National Resource Center for Rural Elderly.

Coward, R. T., Bull, C. N., Kukulka, G., & Galliher, J. M., (Eds.). (1994). *Health services for rural elders.* New York: Springer Publishing Co.

Coward, R. T., & Cutler, S. J. (1988). The concept of a continuum of residence: Comparing activities of daily living among the elderly. *Journal of Rural Studies, 4*, 159–168.

Coward, R. T., & Cutler, S. J. (1989). Informal and formal health care systems for the rural elderly. *Health Services Research, 23*, 785–806.

Coward, R. T., Cutler, S. J., & Mullens, R. A. (1990). Residential differences in the composition of the helping networks of impaired elders. *Family Relations, 39*, 44–50.

Coward, R. T., Duncan, R. P., & Freudenberger, K. M. (1994). Residential differences in the use of formal services prior to entering a nursing home. *The Gerontologist, 34*, 44–49.

Coward, R. T., Duncan, R. P., & Netzer, J. K. (1993). The availability of health care resources for elders living in nonmetropolitan persistent low-income counties in the South. *Journal of Applied Gerontology, 12*, 368–387.

Coward, R. T., Duncan, R. P., & Uttaro, R. (1996). The rural nursing home industry: A national description. *Journal of Applied Gerontology, 15*, 153–171.

Coward, R. T., & Dwyer, J. W. (1991). *Health programs and services for elders in rural America: A review of the life circumstances and formal services that affect the health and well-being of elders.* Kansas City, MO: National Resource Center for Rural Elderly.

Coward, R. T., & Rathbone-McCuan, E. (1985). Delivering health and human services to the elderly in rural society. In R. T. Coward & G. R. Lee (Eds.), *The elderly in rural society: Every fourth elder* (pp. 197–222). New York: Springer Publishing Co.

Coward, R. T., Vogel, W. B., Duncan, R. P., & Uttaro, R. (1995). Should intrastate funding formulae for the Older Americans Act include a rural factor? *The Gerontologist, 35*, 24–34.

Crandall, L. A., Dwyer, J. W., & Duncan, R. P. (1990). Recruitment and retention of rural physicians: Issues for the 1990s. *Journal of Rural Health, 6* , 19–38.

Cutler, S. J., & Coward, R. T. (1988). Residence differences in the health status of elders. *Journal of Rural Health, 4* , 11–26.

Dwyer, J. W. and Coward, R. T. (Eds.) (1992). *Gender, families, and elder care.* Newbury Park, CA: Sage Publications.

Dwyer, J. W., Lee, G. R., & Coward, R. T. (1990). The health status, health services utilization, and support networks of the rural elderly: A decade review. *Journal of Rural Health, 6*, 378–398.

Fickenscher, K. M. (1992). Medical education and preparation of physicians for rural practice. In L. A. Straub & N. Walzer (Eds.), *Rural health care: Innovation in a changing environment* (pp. 77–89). Westport, CT: Praeger.

Gesler, W. M., & Ricketts, T. C. (1992). *Health in rural North America: The geography of health care services and delivery.* New Brunswick, NJ: Rutgers University Press.

Glazer, N. Y. (1990). The home as workshop: Women as amateur nurses and medical care providers. *Gender and Society, 4*, 479–499.

Greene, V. L. (1984). Premature institutionalization among the rural elderly in Arizona. *Public Health Reports, 99*, 58–63.

Hamon R. R., & Blieszner, R. (1990). Filial responsibility expectations among adult child-older parent pairs. *Journal of Gerontology, 45*, P110–P112.

Hewitt, M. (1989). *Defining "rural" areas: Impact on health care policy and research.* Office of Technology Assessment, Washington, DC: U. S. Government Printing Office.

Hicks, L. L. (1990). Availability and accessibility of rural health care. *Journal of Rural Health, 6*, 485–505.

Jensen, L. (1991). The double jeopardized: Nonmetropolitan blacks and Mexicans. In C. B. Flora & J. A. Christenson (Eds.), *Rural policies for the 1990s* (pp. 181–193). Boulder, CO: Westview.

Krout, J. A. (1986). *The aged in rural America.* Westport, CT: Greenwood.

Krout, J. A. (1994). Rural aging community-based services. In R. T. Coward, C. N. Bull, G. Kukulka, & J. M. Galliher, (Eds.), *Health services for rural elders* (pp. 84–107). New York: Springer Publishing Co.

Lassey, W. R., & Lassey, M. L. (1985). The physical health status of the rural elderly. In R. T. Coward & G. R. Lee (Eds.), *The elderly in rural society: Every fourth elder (pp. 83–104).* New York: Springer Publishing Co.

Lee, G. R., Dwyer, J. W., & Coward, R. T. (1990). Residential location and proximity to children among impaired elderly parents. *Rural Sociology, 55*, 579–589.

Lee, G. R., & Lassey, M. L. (1980). Rural-urban differences among the elderly: Economic, social, and subjective factors. *Journal of Social Issues, 36*, 62–73.

Leinbach, R. M. (1988). Differences in need among the rural and urban aged: Statistical versus practical significance. *Journal of Rural Health, 4*, 27–34.

Leonfanti, F. L., & Chiesa, M. E. (1988). Neuguen, Argentina: Provincial health policies and their results. *Journal of Rural Health, 4*, 59–69.

Longino, C. F., Jr., & Smith, M. H. (1994). Epilogue: Reflections on health services for rural elders. In R. T. Coward, C. N. Bull, G. Kukulka, & J. M. Galliher (Eds.), *Health services for rural elders* (pp. 233–241). New York: Springer Publishing Co.

Lundberg, G. D. (1994). United States health care systems reform: An era of shared sacrifice and responsibility begins. *Journal of the American Medical Association, 271,* 1530–1533.

McLaughlin, D. K., & Jensen, L. (1993). Poverty among older Americans: The plight of nonmetropolitan elders. *Journal of Gerontology: Social Sciences, 48,* S44–S54.

Mercier, J. M., Paulson, L., & Morris, E. W. (1988). Rural and urban elderly: Differences in the quality of the parent-child relationship. *Family Relations, 37,* 68–72.

Movassaghi, H., & Kindig, D. (1989). Medical practice and satisfaction of physicians in sparsely populated rural counties in the United States: Results of a 1988 survey. *Journal of Rural Health, 5,* 125–136.

Nelson, G. M. (1980). Social services to the urban and rural aged: The experience of area agencies on aging. *The Gerontologist, 20,* 200–207.

Nelson, G. M. (1983). A comparison of Title XX services to the urban and rural elderly. *Journal of Gerontological Social Work, 6,* 3–23.

Nelson, G. M. (1994). In-home services for rural elders. In R. T. Coward, C. N. Bull, G. Kukulka, & J. M. Galliher (Eds.), *Health services for rural elders* (pp.65–83). New York: Springer Publishing Co.

Rivlin, A., Wiener, J., Hanley, R., & Spence, D. (1988). *Caring for the disabled elderly: Who will pay?* Washington, DC: Brookings.

Rowland, D., & Lyons, B. (1989). Triple jeopardy: Rural, poor, and uninsured. *Health Services Research, 23,* 975–1004.

Sharp, T. S., Halpert, B. P., & Breytspraak, L. (1988). Impact of Medicare's prospective system and the farm crisis on the health care of the elderly: A case study. *The Journal of Rural Health, 4,* 45–56.

Shaughnessy, P. W. (1994). Changing institutional long-term care to improve rural health care. In R. T. Coward, C. N. Bull, G. Kukulka, & J. M. Galliher (Eds.), *Health services for rural elders* (pp. 144–181). New York: Springer Publishing Co.

Stoller, E. P. (1983). Parental caregiving by adult children. *Journal of Marriage and the Family, 45,* 851–858.

Stoller, E. P., & Lee, G. R. (1994). Informal care of rural elders. In R. T. Coward, C. N. Bull, G. Kukulka, & J. M. Galliher (Eds.), *Health services for rural elders* (pp. 33–64). New York: Springer Publishing Co.

Stone, R., Cafferata, G. L., & Sangl, J. (1987). Caregivers of the frail elderly:

A national profile. *The Gerontologist, 27,* 616–626.

Taietz, P., & Milton, S. (1979). Rural-urban differences in the structure and size of services for the elderly in upstate New York. *Journal of Gerontology, 34,* 429–437.

U.S. Senate Special Committee on Aging (1992). *Common beliefs about rural elderly: Myth or fact?* (Serial No. 102–N). Washington, DC: U.S. Government Printing Office.

Wallace, R. B., & Colsher, P. L. (1994). Improving ambulatory and acute care services for the rural elderly: Current solutions, research, and policy directions. In R. T. Coward, C. N. Bull, G. Kukulka, & J. M. Galliher (Eds.), *Health services for rural elders* (pp. 108–126). New York: Springer Publishing Co.

Wright, J. S., & Jablonowski, A. R. (1987). The rural-urban distribution of health professionals in Georgia. *The Journal of Rural Health, 3,* 53–70.

The Role of the Family in Rural Long-Term Care

3

Eleanor Palo Stoller

Although rarely counted in estimates of the cost of long-term care, family members are the primary source of assistance for rural elders living in community settings. These unpaid caregivers assist frail older people in carrying out activities of daily living and provide both instrumental and emotional support in times of illness (Horowitz, 1985). In this chapter, I explore the role of family members as providers of long-term care in rural environments. The chapter begins with an overview of family resources available in rural communities and the ways in which frail rural elders use these resources to configure helping networks. I then explore six issues that require attention if we are to utilize fully the potential of families as care providers. Finally, gaps in our knowledge are identified and an agenda for future research is presented.

FAMILY RESOURCES IN RURAL COMMUNITIES

Husbands and Wives

Spouses are the first line of defense for older people coping with declining health and functional capacity, and rural elders, particularly those living on farms, are more likely to be married than older people living in other residential settings. Part of this difference reflects the fact that rural elderly tend to be younger and have not yet experienced widowhood (Coward, Cutler, & Schmidt,

1989). Higher rates of married status among rural elders also reflect lower rates of divorce in rural than in urban areas, particularly among farmers (Coward et al., 1989).

Not all rural elders have equal access to assistance from a spouse. First, not all older rural people married. Although rates of lifelong singlehood are relatively low among older rural women, they are comparatively high among older rural men (Coward et al., 1989). This gender difference reflects the lower probability of marriage among farm laborers. Farm owners and operators have very high rates of marriage, reflecting dependence on spouses in the farming enterprise (Stoller & Lee, 1994). The advantage of high rates of marriage among rural women, however, is offset by higher rates of widowhood, rates that reflect gender differences in life expectancy, the tendency of women to marry older men, and higher rates of remarriage among widowers. As a result, elderly men are almost twice as likely to be married as elderly women, whereas elderly women are nearly twice as likely to be widowed (Coward, Cutler, & Mullens, 1990).

Adult Children

When a spouse is unavailable or unable to provide the necessary level of support, adult children, particularly daughters, provide help to their frail parents (Horowitz, 1985). Rural elders tend to have more children than their urban counterparts (Clifford, Heaton, Boxx, & Fuguitt, 1985), and they are less likely to be childless (Lee, Dwyer, & Coward, 1990). They do not, however, have more geographically proximate children. Children growing up in rural and small town environments often face limited economic opportunities and move to more urban areas in pursuit of education and occupational advancement. Older farmers are an exception to this rural-urban difference. Farm elders often live with or near one child, usually a son, who is often a partner in the farming enterprise and who will eventually inherit the farm (Lee, Dwyer, & Coward, 1990).

The smaller number of geographically proximate adult children in rural nonfarm and small town areas can also reflect migration patterns of older parents (Coward, Lee, & Dwyer, 1993). Some rural elders without proximate children are people who retired to rural vacation spots. These "amenity migrants" are generally recently retired, married people in relatively good health and with higher than average levels of income and education (Longino, 1990). Some percentage of these elders will return to their community of origin or move to the residential area of an adult child if they encounter poor health, widowhood, and declining financial resources (Litwak & Longino, 1987).

Other Relatives

Less is known about residential variation in relations with kin other than adult children. Extended kin are most important among widowed elders and among elders without proximate children (Kivett, 1985; Litwak, 1985; Matthews, 1987), a situation more common in those rural areas in which restricted economic opportunities encourage the out-migration of young people. Powers and Kivett (1992) report that expectations of support from kin beyond the sibling level are more limited than expectations from primary kin. Although few of their respondents expected secondary kin to provide a home, help out financially, or provide long-term care, a larger proportion felt these kin should visit and help during crises such as illness.

Extended kin are also pivotal in the helping networks of African American elders. Dilworth-Anderson (1992) synthesizes evidence on systems of mutual aid characterizing networks of extended kin within African American communities. The grandfather role also assumes greater salience within African American families (Jackson, 1986), a difference Kivett (1991, p. S256) attributes to the "unconditional status accorded to children . . . as holding the key to the future." Kivett (1991) reports that African American grandfathers gave more help and reported closer relationships but also had greater expectations for assistance from their grandchildren than did white grandfathers. The fact that these differences persisted when controlling for economic resources supports this cultural interpretation.

Assessments of informal networks based on traditional definitions of *family* can overlook informal resources among ethnic groups with greater flexibility in kinship boundaries. A number of researchers, for example, have demonstrated that family bonds are more broadly defined among African Americans, incorporating both extended and "fictive" kin (Chatters, Taylor, & Jackson, 1985). As Collins (1990) explains, African American families see the boundary between households and community as more permeable than do white families. For African Americans, the most significant boundary is that seperating the African American community from the white. Gibson's research confirms that "older black Americans draw from a more varied pool of informal helpers . . . and are more versatile in interchanging helpers for one another as they approach old age" (1986, p. 95).

FAMILY AND THE CONFIGURATION OF HELPING NETWORKS

Helping networks of elderly people in rural areas are more likely to consist exclusively or primarily of informal helpers than are those of older people in urban settings (Blieszner, McCauley, Newhouse, & Mancini, 1987; Coward, Cutler, & Mullens, 1990). Dwyer and Miller (1990b), analyzing data from the 1982 National Long Term Care Survey and the National Survey of Informal Caregivers, found that rural care recipients have fewer paid helpers and receive help with fewer instrumental activities of daily living than care recipients in either small town or urban environments. There are several possible explanations for this pattern. First, the informal networks of rural elders may be "stronger" than those of their urban counterparts and rural residents, consequently, less likely to need formal services. Second, rural older people may rely on their informal networks by default, because formal services are unavailable or insufficient. Finally, rural elders may be more reluctant to accept help from a formal service provider. Evaluating these alternative explanations requires consideration of both formal and informal resources available to rural elders.

The responsiveness of informal networks to the needs of older people is a function of the availability of potential helpers, their willingness to provide assistance, and their access to necessary resources. There is little empirical evidence to support the often cited assumption that rural elders are embedded in stronger informal networks than are their urban counterparts. As we have seen, elderly rural people are more likely than their urban counterparts to be married, but this age-related advantage largely disappears by age 85, the point at which needs for assistance tend to escalate. Rural elders have a larger number of adult children and are less likely to be childless, but there is little evidence that rural residence offers any advantage in access to adult children, many of whom have moved to more urban areas in pursuit of education and employment. In fact, rural nonfarm and small town residents are particularly unlikely to live near adult children. There is some evidence that reliance on extended kin and on friends and neighbors compensates for the absence of adult children among widowed elderly, especially in communities characterized by homogeneity and residential stability (Heller, Quesada, Harvey, & Warner, 1981; Kivett, 1985; Scott & Roberto, 1987). Casarett (1991, p. 249) describes an "ethos of neighborliness" in rural communities which supplies support and assistance and which anticipates other people's needs without their having to ask for help.

The extent to which greater reliance on extended networks can compensate for more limited availability of proximate children depends in part on the resources available to support caregiving efforts. Rural families have fewer financial resources and exhibit higher rates of poverty than their urban counterparts (Coward, 1987). Furthermore, just as geographic distance is a barrier in designing formal services in rural areas, distance adds to the cost of caregiving in both travel time and expense. Higher rates of poverty in rural areas mean that potential helpers have fewer resources with which to overcome distance barriers. They also mean that rural helpers have less time available to assist frail older relatives, friends, or neighbors, since constrained economic resources require greater time in unpaid household works (Stoller, Stoller, Danigelis, & Cutler, 1993).

Rural areas have fewer formal programs to supplement the

efforts of family caregivers. Researchers generally agree that older people living in rural settings are disadvantaged relative to their urban counterparts in both availability and accessibility of home-based and community-based services (Coward & Cutler, 1989; Coward & Rathbone-McCuan, 1985; Krout, 1986), particularly in services targeted to the most severely disabled elderly people (Nelson, 1980). These differences suggest that informal caregivers for rural elderly people face greater responsibilities for providing larger amounts and a broader range of assistance. Research on the configuration of helping networks indicates that older people incorporate formal services when their needs exceed the capacity of their informal networks. This additive pattern of network expansion generally results in a *mixed configuration,* in which the most frail elderly rely on assistance from family, supplemented by formal programs (Johnson & Catalano, 1983; Stoller & Pugliesi, 1988). There is some evidence, however, that a mixed configuration is less common among older people living in rural areas. Coward, Cutler, and Mullins (1990) found that, among the most severely impaired elders, people residing in nonmetropolitan areas were less apt to receive help from a formal provider and were more apt to be receiving assistance exclusively from informal helpers. We do not know the extent to which the lower prevalence of mixed networks reflects preferences of rural elders and their families or limited access to formal programs. We do know, however, that the informal helpers of the most frail rural elders are providing higher levels of care with fewer outside resources than are their urban counterparts.

Although relatively few studies have explored the impact of rural residence on stress and burden among family caregivers, there are several reasons for hypothesizing that caregiving will be more stressful for rural than for urban caregivers. Rural elders exhibit poorer health than their urban counterparts (Coward & Lee, 1985; Krout, 1986). Rural families have fewer financial resources (Coward, 1987), and children of rural elderly are more widely dispersed geographically (Lee & Cassidy, 1985).

Primary caregivers turn to extrafamilial resources when the needs of their older relative exceed their physical and emotional resources (Noelker & Bass, 1989), but formal services are less available in rural areas (Coward & Rathbone-McCuan, 1985), particularly those services with the greatest potential impact on caregiver burden (Montgomery, Gonyea, & Hooyman, 1985). Research on changes in the configuration of networks over time suggests a rural-urban difference in the pace but not the direction of change (Coward, Lee, & Dwyer, 1993). Elderly people in all residential settings exhibit greater reliance on a mixed network of both informal and formal helpers as they experience increasing frailty or disability. This shift, however, occurs more rapidly in urban than in rural communities. As a result, in comparison with their urban counterparts, "rural families face problems of at least equal severity with fewer resources" (Lee, 1988, p. 14). In one of the few studies of burden among rural caregivers, Dwyer and Miller (1990a, 1990b) report that the number of impairments in instrumental activities of daily living is positively related to caregiver burden in both rural and urban settings, but the magnitude of the effect is more than twice as large among rural caregivers.

KEY ISSUES IN UNDERSTANDING INFORMAL CARE AMONG RURAL ELDERS

Reviewing the caregiving literature with a focus on rural families highlights a number of key issues. These include (a) the meaning of independence and control, (b) the importance of reciprocity, (c) concerns about privacy, (d) implications of a gender-based division of labor, (e) the insights of a life course perspective; and (f) the need to consider diversity in rural areas and within rural populations.

The Meaning of Independence and Control

In assessing the consequences of frailty for rural elders, it is important to consider not only the availability of assistance but also the consequences of receiving that assistance. For many frail elders, increasing frailty means a loss of autonomy. People who have managed independently for seven or eight decades feel they are losing control of their lives when adult children and other helpers assume more and more responsibility for decision making. Shenk (1987) reports that her elderly rural respondents "seemed to feel better about those situations in which they made a conscious choice" about seeking assistance. "Arrangements that maximize their personal independence and control seem to be preferred" (p. 17).

Gerontologists sometime assume that older rural people are reluctant to use formal services because of their strong commitment to values of self-reliance and their lack of experience in negotiating bureaucracies (Hansen & Sauer, 1985). Informal care by family members is viewed as preferable because family care allows older people to maintain their independence. But reliance on informal help provided by family members can also undermine feelings of independence and control, particularly if that assistance is being orchestrated by adult children without sufficient consultation with the older parent. This situation is encapsulated in the frequently heard statement, "I don't know what I'm going to do about my mother."

Some older people do, indeed, avoid contact with formal services because they fear institutional placement, the ultimate threat to independence. But reliance on help from adult children also undermines autonomy. The issue is less one of the degree of independence than it is the source of dependence (Lee, 1988). A frail older widow who relies on her daughter for assistance with household chores and her son for help with home repairs and financial management can remain independent of the formal sector, but she is clearly dependent on her adult children. As Lee reminds us, "there is no doubt that for older people, declining health and the consequent inability to manage for themselves are demoralizing experiences, regardless of the source of the assistance they receive" (1988, p. 7).

Rural practitioners must recognize the centrality of rural values of self-reliance and independence. Service providers can enhance the self-esteem of older clients by sensitizing family members to the older person's need to maximize autonomy. It is important to teach caregivers, particularly adult children, to help their older parents while "allowing [them] to remain in control . . . and without appearing to usurp [their] responsibilities" (Mercier & Powers,

1984, p. 174). This means encouraging older parents to do as much as possible for themselves, even at the cost of additional time and some compromise in performance standards. It also means consulting parents before making unilateral decisions. Family caregivers can learn to empower their older relatives by reinforcing a strong identity and encouraging active decision making (Blues & Zerwekh, 1984). The question of what to do about mother is reformulated as "How do you perceive your situation and what can we do to help you improve it." Solving problems sometimes involves a conflict in values, with older parents emphasizing independence and autonomy and adult children emphasizing safety and security. This is particularly the case when geographic mobility has turned adult children into long-distance caregivers. Formal providers may need to advocate for an older parent's right to self-determination, as long as they are able to make informed decisions regarding this trade-off.

The Importance of Reciprocity

The need for assistance can become stressful when one is no longer able to reciprocate for the help one receives (Brown, 1990). Caregiving emerges gradually from long-term patterns of mutual assistance. Until their seventies, older people are net "givers" rather than net "receivers" of goods and services (Van Willigen, 1989). Even when they are no longer capable of reciprocating to the extent that they did in the past, older people often use token gestures to maintain a semblance of reciprocity and to bolster their self-esteem. Wentowski (1981) describes an elderly informant who gives an occasional jar of jelly to the neighbor who takes her shopping every week:

> The necessity of providing something in return, no matter how small, is expressed in the oft repeated statement, "I can't do much, but I try to do what I can." Indeed, if helpers refuse to accept token reciprocations, older people are put in the position of "accepting charity" and some refuse further assistance. (1981, p. 606)

Older people without proximate kin sometimes attempt to ensure support from friends and neighbors by building up obligations through small favors. Francis reports such a process among the older Jewish women she studied:

> A strict code of reciprocity governs these exchanges. . . . Many tenants realize that as they get older, they may have to rely more on neighbors, and they recognize the need to forge new relationships as a type of social insurance. Utilizing this code of reciprocity, they initiate kindness in order to create good will and even indebtedness. (1981, p. 98)

Reciprocity in relationships with friends and neighbors is especially important in rural environments. First, as we have seen, rural elders, particularly in rural nonfarm and small-town settings, have fewer geographically proximate adult children. Furthermore, exchanges of assistance are part of the ethos of neighborliness in rural communities (Casarett, 1991). Descriptions of "neighboring" in the empirical literature reveal several key dimensions of this relationship in rural areas. Help during periods of illness is "just expected" (Brown, 1990, p.60) and should be provided without the recipient having to ask for assistance (Casarett, 1991). Assistance is given in the form of a gift, not as charity (Casarett, 1991). These three features enable extremely frail rural elders to maintain a sense of independence, despite their reliance on a fairly extensive network of informal support, as illustrated by a 92-year-old frail rural widow interviewed by Casarett (1991): "Charlie Taylor, he just came by to mow my lawn. I didn't ask, and he never offered— just did it. Now you know, I don't need no help, I manage just fine. But it sure was nice of him. Folks around here sure do take care of their own" (p. 249).

A fourth dimension of neighborliness poses a potential threat to perceptions of independence. Rural folk can count on help during illness, because it is "expected that the recipient will do the same for someone else in [similarly unspoken] need" (Brown, 1990, p. 60). This expectation prescribes reciprocity. With declines in health status, however, older people not only require more support but find it increasingly difficult to reciprocate. Failure to reciprocate involves a loss of independence. As one of Brown's respondents explained, "this would be the hardest thing. . . . it would mean loss of self-respect. You would feel obligated to someone, you would owe them" (1990, p. 60).

Reciprocity can be measured over the long- as well as the short-term, and frail elders receive help from people whom they helped throughout their lives. While lack of current reciprocity may not interrupt assistance to older people, the shift from net giver to net recipient changes the nature of longstanding exchange relationships and emphasizes the consequences of health-related declines.

Paying for services is an alternative mechanism for reciprocating for informal assistance. For example, Shenk's (1987) respondents indicated that paying a neighbor who helped with shopping or housework allowed them to feel independent. Professionals concerned with maximizing effectiveness of informal networks can encourage helpers to accept payment when offered. They can interpret unreasonably small sums as token payments that reflect past labor market experiences that have failed to keep pace with a service-based economy (Shenk, 1987). Relatives, friends or neighbors, or even volunteers who are uncomfortable about accepting cash payments might agree to be reimbursed for gasoline or other expenses, particularly if they understand the older person's feelings and need to reciprocate.

Concerns about Privacy

Although research on urban neighborhoods has challenged the assumption that rural communities are more closely integrated than urban communities, maintaining anonymity is clearly more difficult in rural settings (Parker et al., 1992). "Living in small communities where everyone knows everyone else, [rural elders] are very concerned about public opinion and the impressions on their neighbors and friends," Shenk explains (1987, p.23). Given the emphasis on values of independence and responsibility for one's own fate (Brown, 1990; Moen, 1978), rural elders are more often embarrassed by age-related changes in their ability to cope with challenges of everyday life than are their urban counterparts.

Coupled with the reluctance to accept help for which they are unable to reciprocate, concerns about privacy would seem to suggest a preference for formal services. Assistance from formal providers lets frail elders avoid revealing to family and friends either the nature or extent of their impairment. But formal services are most acceptable when older people retain decision-making power (Shenk, 1987), a goal that can contradict efforts to coordinate family and formal resources through case management. Parker and colleagues (1992) warn that, because of the difficulty of maintaining privacy and the centrality of values stressing independence and self-reliance, rural elderly people prefer to manage care themselves. Shenk's (1987) research in central Minnesota supports these concerns. The elderly rural women whom she interviewed indicated not only a willingness to use formal services but also a preference for the formal system for personal care tasks. At the same time, they emphasized their desire to make their own decisions about which services they wanted and their reluctance to be "drawn into an all-encompassing system of social services . . . where they will lose control over their choices." Shenk concludes that "services which are provided on a piecemeal basis are more likely to be acceptable" (p. 23).

Implications of a Gender-Based Division of Labor

Rural couples express more traditional attitudes regarding familial roles, decision making, and the division of domestic labor between spouses than do older urban couples (Bescher-Donnelly & Smith, 1981; Dorfman & Heckert, 1988; Lee & Cassidy, 1985; Powers, Keith, & Goudy, 1981; Schumm & Bollman, 1981). Among rural couples, men are more traditional than women (Scanzoni & Arnett, 1987). Among older married couples, wives generally maintain responsibility for cooking meals, washing dishes and clothes, and cleaning the house, while older husbands retain responsibility for yard work, car maintenance, and house repairs (Brubaker & Kinsel, 1988). A division of labor based on gender is especially pronounced among farm couples, a reflection of their interdependence in the farming enterprise (Fitchen, 1991).

This more rigidly segregated division of domestic labor can escalate strains of caregiving among rural couples, since the need to undertake new responsibilities will be more pronounced. Incapacity of a husband means that wife-caregivers assume greater responsibility for stereotypically male tasks, such as yard work, household repairs, and financial management. Husband-caregivers are faced with a need to assume responsibility for more household chores. Because the wife is almost always responsible for the home, even if she delegates some tasks, the disability of a wife means the couple has lost a manager of domestic production.

Studies of spousal caregiving suggest that wives are more likely than husbands to feel guilty about not doing enough or to feel personal responsibility for their spouse's well-being (George & Gwyther, 1986; Miller, 1990). Given the more traditional division of labor and shortage of formal services to supplement their efforts, rural wives may need help in setting limits to their caregiving. Because older wives maintain responsibility for the majority of domestic work, changes in the gender-based division of labor are most dramatic if the husband is the caregiver (Rexroat & Shehan, 1987; Szinovacz, 1989). Husbands must not only increase the range and amount of household work, they also must assume responsibility for tasks defined—and possibly devalued—as woman's work. Hogstel (1985) suggests that programs for older husbands caring for their wives will be more effective if they involve all male groups in which routine household skills, including meal preparation, can be shared as "things that work for me" or "ways to save time."

Mastering new tasks and demonstrating self-reliance can enhance a spouse caregiver's sense of competence and self-esteem (Moss, Lawton, Dean, Goodman, & Schneider, 1987). This potential benefit can be eroded, however, when the dependent spouse is reluctant to give up responsibility, a situation more likely to occur in marriages like those in rural settings, which have been characterized by a fairly rigid division of household labor. Frustrated watching someone intrude on what has been his or her domain, the disabled spouse may criticize the caregiver's task performance, and disagreements can emerge around standards of cleanliness or styles of task performance (Hooyman & Lustbader, 1986).

Studies of gender differences in spousal caregiving suggest that husband caregivers are more likely than wives to receive supplemental support from both formal and informal sources (Johnson & Catalano, 1983; Stoller & Cutler, 1992; Zarit, Reever, & Bach-Peterson, 1986). They are also more likely than wives to receive attention and praise, "since their caregiving tends to be viewed as an unexpected expression of compassion" (Hooyman, 1989, p. 9). In contrast, the wife's caregiving efforts are expected and unnoticed (Guberman, 1988). The impact of more traditional gender roles and the comparative invisibility of women's caregiving is heightened by the limited availability of formal services. Under conditions of scarcity, allocations of formal services are made not only on the basis of the older person's needs but also on the basis of the caregiver's expected ability to cope (Lingson, 1989). Women are often judged as more capable than men of handling caregiving responsibilities on their own (Olesen, 1989; Oliver, 1983). Applying this finding to elderly rural couples suggests that wives caring for impaired husbands will receive fewer supplemental services and will be at particular risk for care-related stress.

On the other hand, women often enter the caregiver role with more support resources than men (Antonucci & Akiyama, 1987; Depner & Ingersoll-Dayton, 1988). In their study of rural men and women caring for spouses with multiple sclerosis, Weinert and Long (1993) found that men with ill wives relied more heavily on their spouses and appeared less able to rely on other people for support. They concluded that "men with chronically ill wives appear to need special help in developing and accepting support from persons other than their wives" (p. 53).

Insights of a Life Course Perspective

Too often studies of older rural families emphasize current characteristics or rural-urban comparisons and overlook the past experiences of current cohorts of older people. In contrast, a life course perspective emphasizes the ways in which people's location in the social system, the historical period in which they live, and their unique personal biographies shape their experience of old age (Stoller & Gibson, 1994).

A life course perspective reminds us of the importance of the historical period in which people lived. People who are the same age experienced particular segments of history at the same stage of life, and they experienced life transitions within similar sociohistorical contexts. Today's cohort of rural elders were born during the first three decades of the 20th century. They experienced their marriage and childbearing years during the Great Depression of the 1930s. They witnessed both migration to industrial centers of the North and West during the 1930s and 1940s, and the subsequent "migration turnaround" during the 1960s and 1970s. Depending on where they live, these cohorts of rural elders have experienced rural industrialization, in-migration of affluent retirees, and cyclical shifts in local economic bases. They felt the effects of the farm crisis of the 1980s, which influenced not only farm families but the merchants and service providers dependent on an agricultural economic base (Lorenz, Conger, Montague & Wickrama, 1993). Some saw their children forced to sell land which their parents and grandparents had farmed (Meyer, 1988). Understanding current cohorts of rural elders demands attention to the impact of these sociohistorical events on the biographies of individuals.

A life course perspective also calls attention to the adaptive resources older people developed as they grew up and grew old. Some of these adaptive resources are strong interpersonal relationships and social supports, beneficial personal coping strategies and behaviors, personal and family values, and economic security (Stoller & Gibson, 1994). The previous discussion of the ethos of neighborliness provides one example. The concept of hardiness offers another. *Hardiness* is defined as "a constellation of personality characteristics that function as a resistance resource in the encounter with stressful life events" (Kobasa, Maddi, & Kahn, 1982, p. 169). Bigbee (1991) suggests that hardiness as a coping resource is consistent with the emphasis in rural culture on independence, self-reliance, and self-care.

Today's cohorts of elderly African Americans developed adaptive strategies that enabled them to survive in a social context characterized by racism but at the same time to maintain their personal integrity (Stoller & Gibson, 1994). Older African Americans spent much of their lives meeting the challenges of a racially segregated world, in which they struggled to maintain self-respect while avoiding direct challenges to the rules for "living Jim Crow" (Wright, 1937/1991). Special adaptive resources were called into play to deal with these stressors, and these resources affected the aging experience (Stoller & Gibson, 1994). Strong informal networks are one example of these adaptive resources. Carleton-LaNey (1992, p. 520) explains that

> a history of injustices, supported and often initiated by "the government" has caused elderly blacks to develop a healthy sense of paranoia. To avoid the expected humiliation of racism that is often inherent in formal helping systems, they have established and relied on their own network of helpers.

Lifelong barriers to medical care in rural areas have also strengthened resources for managing illness outside the medical care delivery system. Prior to World War II, health care tended to be delivered by women, with remedies handed down from generation to generation (Newbern, 1991). As one of Newbern's informants explains: "Life was hard . . . we had enough to eat, but there was practically no cash money . . . too many of us to go running to the doctor like folks do now" (p. 65). Newbern reports that illnesses were treated at home and physicians consulted as a last resort.

Data from more recent health surveys indicate that only 10% to 25% of all illness episodes actually result in contacts with professional health providers, and a large proportion of those who seek medical care have treated themselves before seeking professional advice (Dean, 1981; DeFriese & Woomert, 1983). Patterns of lay care continue to be important in rural environments. Rural elders report more limitations in activities of daily living and a higher prevalence of chronic conditions than their urban counterparts, yet have more limited access to formal medical resources (Lee, Dwyer,

& Coward, 1990). Self-care and reliance on lay healers have been particularly important in rural areas where geographic distance, poor transportation, and limited financial resources restricted access to formal providers (Newbern, 1991). A recent evaluation of self-care practices among rural and small-town elderly in upstate New York indicated that most decisions regarding lay management of symptoms were appropriate and that fewer than one in eight older respondents were judged at possible risk for not consulting a physician regarding one or more of their symptoms (Stoller, Forster, Pollow, & Tisdale, 1993).

The Need to Consider Diversity in Rural Life

A clear understanding of family care for older people also requires recognition of diversity among rural environments and rural people. Rural areas differ along a number of dimensions that influence the configuration of care, including population density, proximity to metropolitan areas, economic base, regional culture, and migration patterns. For example, the out-migration of young people from rural areas of the Northeast and Midwest decreases the number of proximate siblings who can share responsibility for caring for their frail older parents and converts adult children into long-distance caregivers (Coward & Dwyer, 1990). Cyclical economic shifts in regions depending on mining, for another example, generate cohort differences in the out-migration of youth. In regions dependent on mining, few young people leave during periods when mining companies are hiring, but many migrate in search of education and employment during periods of contraction. Differences in regional culture and historical patterns of migration also have been cited as explanations of the greater reliance of southern elderly people, particularly African Americans, on siblings, friends and neighbors as sources of informal care (Chatters, Taylor, & Jackson, 1985).

Rural populations can also vary on a number of sociodemographic variables, both within and among geographic regions. Racial and ethnic differences, for example, can structure patterns of informal interaction and influence values and attitudes toward family caregiving (Stoller & Lee, 1993). Hierarchies based on race and ethnicity influence availability of resources with which to implement these values. Relatively affluent older people not only enter old age in better health but have more resources to pay for medical care and hire private-sector help (Stoller & Cutler, 1993). Economically disadvantaged older people too often cope with poor health within a context of more limited medical care, substandard housing, inadequate nutrition, and unreliable transportation (Stoller & Lee, 1993).

Interaction among these sources of diversity highlights the importance of sensitivity to local or regional characteristics in designing interventions to supplement or support the efforts of family caregivers. Relatively affluent agricultural regions of the Midwest differ dramatically from economically depressed rural regions of Appalachia. Ethnicity is also confounded with geographic region. Rural African Americans are concentrated in the South, older rural Chicanos in the Southwest. Although older Native American populations are located across a broad range of rural areas, the geographic concentration of particular tribal groups produces regional differences in cultural heritage, including family structure and values. Unfortunately, the current state of knowledge concerning informal care in rural areas does not permit researchers or practitioners to disentangle the effects of rural residence from the effects of local or regional characteristics (Coward et al., 1990).

CONCLUSIONS

Directions for Research

This synthesis of the literature on the role of families as providers of long-term care for frail rural elders suggests several directions for future development. From a research perspective, we can identify a number of unanswered questions. Perhaps the most urgent need is for research into rural/urban differences in the sources of assistance for frail or infirm older people. Most elderly people who live in rural areas require little assistance from others, and many of those who do require assistance receive it from their spouses or children. What happens to rural elders who need assistance from other sources because spouses and children are unavailable? Do those who live in rural areas move toward formal or informal sources of support? Compared to urban counterparts, are they more likely to be institutionalized at any given level of disability? Do they find sufficient assistance in their communities through friends, neighbors, and the formal service network, or do they struggle with higher levels of unmet need than urban elders? Existing research does not provide answers to these questions.

A number of other questions concerning the configuration of helping networks among rural elders remain unanswered. We need to understand more about the process whereby helpers are recruited or assume caregiving responsibilities and the ways in which these selection processes vary by residential setting. Although investigators agree that family and friends provide most of the assistance received by frail elderly people living in rural settings, many of whom have only limited access to formal programs, little is known about the adequacy of that care in meeting the needs of older care recipients. More information also is needed about the consequences of providing care to rural caregivers who provide support for severely impaired care recipients with fewer supplementary formal services than their urban counterparts.

Answering these questions will require more studies utilizing qualitative methods. We need to listen to the voices of frail rural elders and their family caregivers in order to understand the meanings they attach to the experiences of giving and receiving care. Just as policy experts have cautioned against exporting scaled-down versions of urban services into rural environments, researchers must be cautious about employing structured questionnaires developed on urban populations in eliciting information about rural families.

Most of the research on rural families has been based on regional samples, and the few studies that have employed national samples have not controlled for region. It is entirely possible, given the conflicting results of many regional studies, that there are marked differences in the proximity of children, frequency of interaction with children, and actual exchange of assistance between generations across different regions of the country. In particular, it is likely that rural residents in the East and Southeast are more firmly embedded in networks of children and other kin, while those in the West and Midwest have less access to support from these sources (Heller et al., 1981). Rural environments cannot be treated as uniform or homogeneous, and studies that systematically compare the family relations of rural elders across regions of the country are very much needed.

Greater attention should also be directed toward issues of diversity within the rural population. As researchers have begun to recognize, the "rural" category incorporates variation along multiple dimensions. In addition to examining differences in informal care among farm, rural nonfarm, and small-town settings, we need to examine the impact of economic base, social-class differences, proximity to a metropolitan center, population density, historical patterns of migration and residential stability, existence of ethnic subcultures and minority populations, and regional subcultures on family care of frail rural elders. We need to learn more about the impact of multiple systems of inequality on the ways in which rural elders configure support networks. As Stoller and Gibson (1994) point out, inequality involves privilege as well as disadvantage. We know that economically disadvantaged elderly people too often cope with poor health within a context of relatively more limited medical care, substandard housing, inadequate nutrition, and unreliable transportation. Furthermore, similar hardships among members of poor, rural elders' informal networks limit the ability of these helpers to respond to the older person's needs, regardless of supporting values or strength of commitment. We know less about the impact of financial resources on the configuration of support networks among more affluent rural elders.

Directions for Policy and Program Development

This review of the literature suggests a number of issues to be considered in designing programs to support the efforts of rural caregivers. Program planners sometimes assume that a program developed in an urban environment can be scaled down and exported to a rural setting. Researchers, in contrast, have stressed the need to design programs which recognize not only the general barriers to service delivery in rural areas but also acknowledge features unique to local areas, including environmental, social, political and economic conditions (Coward, 1982; Nofz, 1986). To be successful, services designed to enhance caregiving efforts of rural families must address meaningful concerns through methods consistent with rural values and rural lifestyles (Weinert & Long, 1987).

Successful programs must recognize the importance of informal networks and the centrality of self-reliance and independence. Because many rural families are caring for severely impaired older relatives with little or no outside help, rural caregivers can benefit from indirect services. Training caregivers in basic home-nursing skills both improves the quality of care and enhances the sense of competence and mastery of caregivers. As discussed above, professionals can also sensitize family members to the older person's need to reciprocate and to maximize autonomy.

The almost exclusive reliance of rural elders on informal assistance, even at high levels of disability, raises concerns about the physical and emotional toll on family caregivers. Coward, Cutler, and Mullins (1990) remind us that respite programs have met with limited success in rural areas and urge rural practitioners to "seek creative ways to provide family caregivers with some sort of break from the demands of nearly constant care" (p. 49). Mercier and Powers (1984) describe church programs which offer transportation, companionship, and crisis intervention for rural elders. Such programs may be especially effective among older Blacks, for whom churches play particularly important roles in providing emotional support and instrumental assistance (Wood & Parham, 1990). Other programs emphasize reliance on volunteers to supplement limited formal programs, including greater reliance on churches, voluntary organizations, and natural helpers like clergy and mail carriers. The extent to which these groups or individuals are willing or able to assume these responsibilities, however, remains an empirical question (Stoller & Lee, 1994). In rural communities, use of volunteers can also raise elders' concerns regarding privacy.

Finally, we need not only more research employing a life course perspective but also more programs sensitive to sociohistorical factors. Any recommendations based on current research are bounded in time. The extent to which life course experiences and adaptive resources of current cohorts of rural elders will be relevant to future cohorts remains an empirical question. Continuing research will be needed to assess (a) the future impact of changes in rural environments, including the increasing tendency of farm wives to seek paid employment to supplement income from the farming enterprise; (b) the consequences of rural industrialization and the farm crisis of the 1980s, not only on farm families but also on merchants and service providers; (c) the effects of amenity migration to rural retirement communities; (d) regional shifts in rural economic opportunities and their impact on migration patterns; (e) declining land values and a shrinking tax base; and (f) hospital closures and shortages of health services and personnel (Koff, 1992; National Council on the Aging, 1990). These types of changes will continue to affect the family resources available to frail rural elders, the experiences of providing care, and the types of formal services needed to enhance the capability of family caregivers.

REFERENCES

Antonucci, T., & Akiyama, H. (1987). Social networks in adult life and a preliminary examination of the convoy model. *Journal of Gerontology, 42,* 519–527.

Bescher-Donelly, L., & Smith, L. (1981). The changing role and status of rural women. In R. T. Coward & S. Smith (Eds.), *The family in rural society* (pp.9–26). Boulder, CO: Westview.

Bigbee, J. (1991). The concept of hardiness as applied to rural nursing. In A. Bushy (Ed.), *Rural health nursing* (Vol. 1, pp. 39–48). Newbury

Park, CA: Sage.

Blieszner, R., McAuley, W., Newhouse, J., & Mancini, J. (1987). Rural-urban differences in service use by older adults. In T. Brubaker (Ed.), *Aging, health and family* (pp.162–174), Newbury Park, CA: Sage.

Blues, A., & Zerwekh, J. (1984). *Hospice and palliative nursing care.* Orlando, FL: Grune and Stratton.

Brown, K. (1990). Connected independence: A paradox of rural health? *Journal of Rural Community Psychology, 11*(1), 51–64.

Brubaker, T., & Kinsel, B. (1988). Who is responsible for household tasks in long-term marriages of the young-old elderly? In L. Ade-Ridder & C. Hennon (Eds.). *Lifestyles of the elderly: Diversity in relationships, health and caregiving.* (pp. 97–105) New York: Human Sciences.

Carlton-LaNey, I. (1992). Elderly black farm women: A population at risk. *Social Work, 37,* 517–523.

Casarett, D. (1991). Elders and neighborliness: Implications for rural health care. In A. Bushy (Ed.), *Rural nursing* (Vol. 1. pp. 243–255). Newbury Park, CA: Sage.

Chatters, L., Taylor, R., & Jackson, J. (1985). Size and composition of the informal helping networks of elderly blacks. *Journal of Gerontology, 40,* 605–614.

Clifford, W., Heaton, T., Boxx, P., & Fuguitt, G. (1985). The rural elderly in demographic perspective. In R. T. Coward & G. R. Lee (Eds.), *The elderly in rural society: Every fourth elder* (pp. 25–55). New York: Springer Publishing Co.

Collins, P. (1990). *Black feminist thought: Knowledge, consciousness, and the politics of empowerment.* Boston: Unwin Hyman.

Coward, R. T. (1982). Cautions about the role of natural helping networks in programs for the rural elderly. In N. Stinnett, J. DeFrain, K. King, H. Lingren, G. Rowe, S. VanZandt, & R. Williams (Eds.), *Family strengths 4: Positive support systems* (pp. 291–306). Lincoln, NE: University of Nebraska Press.

Coward, R. T. (1987). Factors associated with the configuration of the helping networks of noninstitutionalized elders. *Journal of Gerontological Social Work, 10,* 113–132.

Coward, R. T., & Cutler, S. (1989). Informal and formal health care systems for the rural elderly. *Health Services Research, 23,* 785–806.

Coward, R. T., Cutler, S.,& Mullens, R. (1990). Residential differences in the composition of the helping networks of impaired elders. *Family Relations, 39,* 44–50.

Coward, R. T., Cutler, S.,& Schmidt, F. (1989). Differences in the household composition of elders by age, gender, and area of residence. *The Gerontologist, 29,* 814–821.

Coward, R. T., & Dwyer, J. (1990). The association of parent care by adult children. *Research on Aging, 12*(2), 158–181.

Coward, R. T., & Lee, G. (1985). *The elderly in rural society: Every fourth elder.* New York: Springer Publishing Co.

Coward, R. T., Lee, G., & Dwyer, J. (1993). The family relations of rural elders. In C. N. Bull (Ed.), *Aging in rural America* (pp. 216–231). Newbury Park, CA: Sage.

Coward, R. T., & Rathbone-McCuan, E. (1985). Delivering health and human services to the elderly in rural society. In R. Coward & G. Lee (Eds.), *The elderly in rural society: Every fourth elder* (pp. 197–222). New York: Springer Publishing Co.

Dean, K. (1981). Self-care responses to illness: A selected review. *Social Science and Medicine, 15A,* 673–687.

DeFriese, G., & Woomert, A. (1983). Self-care among the U. S. elderly. *Research on Aging, 5,* 3–23.

Depner, C., & Ingersol-Dayton, B. (1988). Supportive relationships in later life. *Psychology and Aging, 3,* 348–357.

Dilworth-Anderson, P. (1992, Summer). Extended kin network in black families. *Generations, 20,* pp. 29–32.

Dorfman, L., & Heckert, D. (1988). Egalitarianism in retired rural couples: Household tasks, decision making and leisure activities. *Family Relations, 37,* 85–92.

Dwyer, J., & Miller, M. (1990a). Determinants of primary caregiver stress and burden: Area of residence and the caregiving networks of frail elders. *Journal of Rural Health, 6,* 161–184.

Dwyer, J., & Miller, M. (1990b). Residential differences in characteristics of the caregiving network: Implications for primary caregiver stress and burden. *Family Relations, 39,* 27–37.

Fitchen, J. (1991). *Endangered spaces, enduring places: Change, identity and survival in rural America.* Boulder, CO: Westview.

Francis, D. (1981). Adaptive strategies of the elderly in England and Ohio. In Christine Fry (Ed.), *Dimensions: Aging, culture and health* (pp. 91–102). Brooklyn: Praeger.

George, L., & Gwyther, L. (1986). Caregiver well-being: A multidimensional examination of family caregivers of demented adults. *The Gerontologist, 26,* 253–259.

Gibson, R. (1986). Outlook for the black family. In A. Pifer & L. Bronte (Eds.), *Our aging society: Paradox and promise* (pp. 181–187). New York: Norton.

Guberman, N. (1988). The family, women and caring: Who cares for the carers? *New Feminist Research, 17*(2), 37–41.

Hansen, S., & Sauer, W. (1985). Children and their elderly parents. In W. J. Sauer & R. T. Coward (Eds.), *Social support networks and the care of the elderly* (pp. 41–66). New York: Springer Publishing Co.

Heller, P., Quesada, G., Harvey, D., & Warner, L. (1981). Familism in rural and urban America: Critique and reconceptualization of a construct. *Rural Sociology, 46,* 446–464.

Hogstel, M. (1985). Older widowers: A small group with special needs. *Geriatric Nursing, 6,* 24–26.

Hooyman, N. (1989, March). *Women, caregiving and equity: A feminist perspective.* Invited presentation at Annual Program Meeting of the Council on Social Work Education, Chicago.

Hooyman, N., & Lustbader, W. (1986). *Taking care: Supporting older people and their families.* New York: Free Press.

Horowitz, A. (1985). Family caregiving to the frail elderly. In M. P. Lawton & G. L. Maddox (Eds.), *Annual Review of Gerontology and Geriatrics, 5,* 194–246.

Jackson, J. (1986). Black grandparents: Who needs them? In R. Staples (Ed.), *The Black family* (3rd ed.). Belmont, CA: Wadsworth.

Johnson, C., & Catalano, D. (1983). A longitudinal study of family supports to impaired elderly. *The Gerontologist, 23,* 612–618.

Kivett, V. (1985). Aging in rural society: Non-kin community relations and participation. In R. T. Coward & G. Lee (Eds.), *The elderly in rural society* (pp. 171–192). New York: Springer Publishing Co.

Kivett, V. (1991). Centrality of the grandfather role among older rural black and white men. *Journal of Gerontology, 46,* S250–258.

Kobasa, S., Maddi, S., & Kahn, S. (1982). Hardiness and health: A prospective study. *Journal of Personality and Social Psychology, 42,* 168–177.

Koff, T. (1992, Spring). Aging in place: Rural issues. *Generations, 20,* pp. 53–55.

Krout, J. (1986). *The aged in rural America.* Westport, CT: Greenwood.

Lee, G. (1988). Kinship ties among older people: The residence factor. In R. Marotz-Baden, C. B. Hennon, & T. H. Brubaker (Eds.), *Families in rural America.* St. Paul, MN: National Council on Family Relations.

Lee, G., & Cassidy, M. (1985). Family and kin relations of the rural elderly. In R. T. Coward & G. Lee (Eds.), *The elderly in rural society* (pp. 151–170). New York: Springer Publishing Co.

Lee, G., Dwyer, J., & Coward, R. T. (1990). Residential location and proximity to children among impaired elderly parents. *Rural Sociology, 55,* 579–589.

Lingson, S. (1989). Filial responsibility in the welfare state. *Journal of Applied Gerontology, 8,* 18–35.

Litwak, E. (1985). *Helping the elderly: The complementary roles of informal networks and formal systems.* New York: Guilford.

Litwak, E., & Longino, C. (1987). Migration patterns among the elderly: A developmental perspective. *The Gerontologist, 27,* 266–272.

Longino, C. (1990). Geographical distribution and migration. In R. H. Binstock & L. K. George (Eds.), *Handbook of aging and the social sciences* (3rd ed., pp. 45–63). New York: Academic Press.

Lorenz, F., Conger, R., Montague, R., & Wickrama, K. (1993). Economic conditions, spouse support, and psychological distress of rural husbands and wives. *Rural Sociology, 58,* 247–268.

Matthews, S. (1987). Provision of care to old parents: Division of responsibility among adult children. *Research on Aging, 9,* 45–80.

Mercier, J., & Powers, E. (1984). The family and friends of rural aged as a natural support system. *Journal of Community Psychology, 12,* 334–346.

Meyer, M. (1988). Implications for assessment: Characteristics of rural families in crisis. *Journal of Rural Community Psychology, 9,* 12–15.

Miller, B. (1990). Gender differences in spouse management of the caregiver role. In E. K. Abel & M. K. Nelson (Eds.), *Circles of care: Work and identity in women's lives* (pp. 92–104). Albany: State University of New York Press.

Moen, E. (1978). The reluctance of the elderly to accept help. *Social Problems, 25,* 293–303.

Montgomery, R., Gonyea, J., & Hooyman, N. (1985). Caregiving and the experience of subjective and objective burden. *Family Relations, 34,* 19–25.

Moss, M., Lawton, M. P., Dean, J., Goodman, M., & Schneider, J. (1987, November). *Satisfaction and burden in caring for impaired elderly persons.* Paper presented at annual scientific meetings of the Gerontological Society of America, Washington, DC.

National Council on the Aging (1990). *Perspectives on aging.* Washington, DC: Author.

Nelson, G. (1980). Social services to the urban and rural aged: The experience of Area Agencies on Aging. *The Gerontologist, 29,* 200–207.

Newbern, V. (1991). Health care in the South: 1900–1945. In A. Bushy (Ed.), *Rural nursing* (Vol. 1, pp. 59–68). Newbury Park, CA: Sage.

Noelker, L., & Bass, D. (1989). Home care for elderly persons: Linkages between formal and informal caregivers. *Journal of Gerontology, 44,* S63–S70.

Nofz, M. (1986). Social services for older rural Americans: Some policy concerns. *Social Work, 26,* 85–91.

Olesen, V. (1989). Caregiving, ethical and informal: Emergent challenges in the sociology of health and illness. *Journal of Health and Social Behavior, 30,* 1–10.

Oliver, J. (1983). The caring wife. In J. Finch & D. Groves (Eds.), *A labour of love: Women, work and caring* (pp. 72–88). London: Routledge.

Parker, M., Quinn, M., Biehl, M., McKinley, A., Hartwell, S., VanHook, R., & Detzner, D. (1992). Issues in rural case management. *Family and Community Health, 14*(4), 40–60.

Powers, E., Keith, P., & Goudy, W. (1981). Family networks of the rural aged. In R. T. Coward & W. M. Smith (Eds.), *The family in rural society* (pp. 119–217). Boulder, CO: Westview.

Powers, E., & Kivett, V. (1992). Kin expectations and kin support among rural older adults. *Rural Sociology, 57,* 194–215.

Rexroat, C., & Shehan, C. (1987). The family life cycle and spouses' time in housework. *Journal of Marriage and the Family, 49,* 735–50.

Scanzoni, J., & Arnett, C. (1987). Policy implications derived from a study of rural and urban marriages. *Family Relations, 36,* 430–436.

Schumm, W., & Bollman, S. (1981). Interpersonal processes in rural families. In R. T. Coward & W. M. Smith (Eds.), *The family in rural society* (pp. 129–145). Boulder, CO: Westview.

Scott, J., & Roberto, K. (1987). Informal supports of older adults: A rural-urban comparison. *Family Relations, 36,* 444–449.

Shenk, D. (1987). *Someone to lend a helping hand: The lives of rural older women in central Minnesota.* St. Cloud, MN: Central Minnesota Council on Aging.

Stoller, E., & Lee, G. (1994). Informal care of rural elders. In R. Coward, C. N. Bull, G. Kukulka, & J. Galliher (Eds.), *Health services for rural elders* (pp. 33–64). New York: Springer Publishing Co.

Stoller, E., & Pugliesi, K. (1988). Informal networks of community based elderly: Changes in composition over time. *Research on Aging, 10,* 499–516.

Stoller, E., & Gibson, R. (1994). *Worlds of difference: Inequality and the aging experience.* Newbury Park, CA: Pine Forge Press.

Stoller, E., & Cutler, S. (1992). The impact of gender on configurations of care among married elderly couples. *Research on Aging, 14,* 313–330.

Stoller, E., & Cutler, S. J. (1993). Predictors of use of paid help among older people living in the community. *The Gerontologist, 33,* 31–40.

Stoller, E., Forster, L., Pollow, R., & Tisdale, W. (1993). Lay evaluation of symptoms by older people: An assessment of potential risk. *Health Education Quarterly, 20,* 505–522.

Stoller E., & Lee, G. (1993) Informal helping networks in rural environments. In R. Coward, C. N. Bull, J. Galliher, & G. Kukulka (Eds.), *Health services for rural elders* (pp. 33–64). New York: Springer Publishing Co.

Stoller, M., Stoller, E., Danigelis, N., & Cutler, S. (1993, November). *Volunteer activity and informal assistance as investment and consumption among elderly people.* Paper presented at annual scientific meetings of the Gerontological Society of America, New Orleans, LA.

Szinovacz, M. (1989). Retirement, couples and household work. In S. J. Bahr & E. Peterson (Eds.), *Aging and the family* (pp. 33–58). Lexington, MA: Lexington.

Van Willigen, J. (1989). *Gettin' some age on me: Social organization of older people in a rural American community.* Lexington, KY: University of Kentucky Press.

Weinert, C., & Long, K. (1987). Understanding the health care needs of rural families. *Family Relations, 36,* 450–455.

Weinert, C., & Long, K. (1993). Support systems for the spouses of chronically ill persons in rural areas. *Family and Community Health, 16*(1), 46–54.

Wentowski, G. (1981). Reciprocity and the coping strategies of older people: Cultural dimensions of network building. *The Gerontologist, 21,* 600–609.

Wood, J., & Parham, I. (1990). Coping with perceived burden: Ethnic and cultural issues in Alzheimer's family caregiving. *Journal of Applied Gerontology, 9,* 325–339.

Wright, R. (1991). The ethics of living Jim Crow. In H. L. Gates, Jr. (Ed.), *Bearing witness: Selections from African-American autobiography in the twentieth century.* New York: Pantheon. (Originally published in 1937)

Zarit, S., Reever, K., & Bach-Peterson, J. (1986). Relatives of the impaired elderly: Correlates of feelings of burden. *The Gerontologist, 20,* 649–655.

The Role of Rural Home- and Community-Based Services

4

Joan K. Magilvy

An integral part of the long-term care continuum for rural older adults is home care. Set in the home and community, rural home care is supported by a variety of community-based services. While not necessarily a cost-effective substitute for institutional long-term care, home care has been shown to enhance quality of life and promote a holistic, family-centered approach to care of frail elders and older adults with post acute, chronic, or terminal illnesses (Benjamin, 1992; Gould, Haslanger, & Vladeck, 1992; Magilvy, Congdon, & Martinez, 1994). In this chapter, I explore the diversity of issues around home- and community-based services for rural older adults within the framework of long-term care research and policy implications. The need for expedient and comprehensive research has been acknowledged by many agencies; the National Institutes of Health (NIH) have promoted activities of the Agency for Health Care Policy and Research (AHCPR), National Institute on Aging (NIA), and National Institute for Nursing Research (NINR). For example, NINR recently published a priorities document for nursing research on long-term care for older adults, including state of the science research reviews on home care, nursing homes, care transitions, and hospitals and community-based services (NINR, 1994). In addition, the NINR is currently preparing a monograph on nursing research priorities in community-based health care models in two selected vulnerable areas: rural and urban inner-city with underserved populations (NINR, 1995).

BACKGROUND AND DEFINITIONS

While definitions of home care and community-based services vary, a common understanding of the terms is essential before proceeding. The wide array of home care services offered in the United States is not always applicable in rural areas, as demonstrated in the following discussion.

Defining Rural Home Care

In this chapter, *home care* is defined as in-home health and supportive services, broadly including post acute, chronic, terminal, and long-term care services provided at home. Home care includes a variety of services, some focusing on health or medical needs and others focusing on social needs, and/or assistance with functional and instrumental daily activities necessary for independent living (Redford & Severns, 1994).

Health or medical home care services can include skilled nursing, home health aide and physical, occupational, and other therapies to assist with recuperative and rehabilitative care. Social supportive home care services include homemaker, chore, meal, and personal care, respite care, and other services oriented around daily activities (Redford & Severns, 1994). Other services available in some rural areas are: social work, volunteer assistance, and counseling. Related to home care is in-home hospice care for terminally ill patients and families, increasingly available in rural communities. Despite the variety of services offered, the medical model predominates in delivery of home care, both rural and urban. It is also important to consider that this discussion demonstrates the range and diversity of home care services in many parts of the country, especially in large urban centers. However, in rural America, the types of services and availability differ. Availability of providers and/or agencies is inconsistent. Geographic considerations, economic variables such as funding and reimbursement mechanisms, and local adaptations in home care provision consistent with regional or local preferences or culture also contribute to diverse patterns of care.

Defining Community-Based Services

The health, social, and supportive services, and informal care described above fit into a definition of *community-based services,* which Krout (1994) identifies as a broad range of services provided outside of institutions that help older adults maintain independent health and functioning. Home care, (home health, hospice, personal care, and homemaker services); nutrition, (congregate and in-home meals); mental health; information and referral, outreach, and case management; senior centers; respite and adult day care; housing (a full range of options); and transportation services are all part of the community-based complex of services (Krout, 1994). These services may be available from a wide range of public and private agencies and persons including volunteers, churches, case management agencies (e.g., Medcaid home- and community-based services programs), hospitals, nursing homes, and home care agencies, community care (e.g., public health nursing services), social services, regional aging services, agricultural extension agencies, and recreational and educational services.

Uncovering the Diversity of Services

Gould and colleagues noted that not all home care is long term; post acute services is an expanding area as managed care puts pressure on hospitals to reduce length of stay and substitute alternative services (Gould et al., 1992). Short-term long-term care (less than 90 days) has taken on growing importance in the home care arena. Hughes (1992) differentiated home care into high tech, low tech, hospice, and longer term skilled care. Not all home care is delivered to elders; adults or children with disabilities, chronic or terminal illness, HIV/AIDS, and developmental delays also receive home care services. Not all home care is delivered at the recipient's own home or apartment; board and care residents receive home care as do elders living with relatives, sharing homes, and residing in different levels of assisted living (Benjamin, 1992). Finally, home care is not limited to formal services provided by professionals, paraprofessionals, and agencies. Rather, 80% of all home care (especially rural) is provided by informal sources, such as family caregivers (Gould et al., 1992; see also Stoller, Chapter 3 in this volume). Krout (1994) warned that not all community-based services are appropriate or cost-efficient in meeting all needs of clients; however, the array of community-based services may allow individuals to remain at home, out of acute and institutional long-term care facilities. Many rural-dwelling older adults strongly prefer to remain at home, although they do not all have equal access to informal and family care services (Krout, 1994; Magilvy et al., 1994; Weinert & Long, 1993).

Issues of emerging types of home care and diversity across groups of consumers have implications for reimbursement, case mix, and personnel in rural areas. In large urban home care agencies, numerous personnel can handle patients of widely diverse ages and expanded case mix situations, reimbursed by a variety of federal, state, private insurance, capitated, and self-pay mechanisms. In rural agencies, however, the availability of personnel with skill levels and knowledge of patients ranging from infants to elders may be limited. The range of reimbursement mechanisms may be limited, or in some cases geographic boundaries may be set that prevent some isolated elders from receiving services. While case mix may be broad, the numbers of patients with diverse diagnoses or ages may be very small, providing nurses and other staff with limited opportunities to gain competence in specialty care. Finally, sharing of services such as public health or primary care among several communities may necessitate creative local solutions to these issues. Research evaluating or highlighting strong community-based models is extremely limited.

Funding Rural Home Care

Funding for home care and community-based services includes four major sources: Medicare; Medicaid; Social Services Block Grants; and the Older Americans Act. Details of these programs and their many funding mechanisms can be found in numerous sources beyond the scope of this chapter (see Benjamin, 1992; Nelson, 1994; Redford & Severns, 1994). Additional support is available from Veterans Administration programs, other programs, HMOs and social HMOs, and holistic services resembling the On-Lok model for elders most at risk (Zawadski & Eng, 1988). Rural home care services for older adults depend heavily on Medicare funding. Medicaid waivers and block grant programs vary widely from state to state, and few experimental or alternatively funded programs exist in these areas. Due to the complexity of need and heterogeneity of rural America, it is imperative to explore alternative models that might fit in selected rural areas.

Several recent reviews of current literature in home care and community-based services for rural older adults have been published. The reader is referred to these books, chapters, and articles for their excellent analyses and recommendations (Coward, Bull, Kukulka, & Galliher, 1994; Gould et al., 1992; Krout, 1994; Nelson, 1994; Ory & Duncker, 1992; Redford & Severns, 1994; Weinert & Burman, 1994). Research on rural home care and community-based services covers aspects of care utilization, distribution, reimbursement for services, and health care professionals and resources. Recently, many issues have been identified that have implications for further research and policy recommendations. In this chapter, I highlight several issues (accessibility of services, cost and organization, quality; coordination of care, and integration of services), discuss research opportunities for each area, and make recommendations for long-term care research and policy. The goal of this discussion is to stimulate the development of a creative vision in seeking solutions to these complex, multifaceted problems.

REVIEW OF MAJOR ISSUES

Accessibility of Services

The issue of access to services by consumers pervades the literature on rural health care and is an important consideration in rural home- and community-based services (HCBS). Many factors have been identified related to accessibility for rural elders.

Krout (1994) listed six "A words" related to accessibility: availability, awareness, appropriateness, acceptability, affordability, and adequacy. The factors or barriers most often identified around rural accessibility are distance from services, geographical barriers and weather, number and distribution of services and providers, and transportation issues. Another problem for rural home- and community-based services is lack of knowledge or awareness of services, especially by physicians and other community gatekeepers as well as patients and families (Magilvy et al., 1994; Redford & Severns, 1994). Services may be unacceptable to rural elders due to reasons such as lack of cultural congruence (differences in the cultural expectations of client and provider), or a level of care that is inappropriate for the condition of the patient (Krout, 1994; Magilvy et al., 1994). For example, Magilvy and colleagues (1994) found that, for some Hispanic elders, living in a nursing home far from their family and community and cared for by staff not fluent in Spanish would be unacceptable. In another example, Congdon and Magilvy (1995) found that rural culture influenced care provision: Privacy issues were raised when rural nurses were members of the communities they served (i.e., they were neighbors as well as professionals). These issues greatly affect the accessibility of rural home care services. Although these factors exist to differing degrees across rural America, the responsibility of delivering accessible services must ultimately be placed upon health care providers. Rural agencies and providers need to identify the barriers and constraining factors most prevalent in their local service delivery area and work to overcome these barriers and constraints to assure accessibility for their clients.

Another influence on accessibility is inability of rural health care services to make needed changes in concert with health care system changes. This may be due to multiple factors of rural life, including administrative difficulties encountered by small agencies serving very large areas (Burman, Steffes, & Weinert, 1994). Hassinger, Hicks, and Godino (1993) reported that the range of available health care services is more restricted for rural than urban residents. However, Salmon, Nelson, and Rous (1993) revisited rural/urban comparisons in the continuum of care and concluded that more differences exist in access and utilization of rural health and in-home services among rural counties and across rural areas than between rural and urban areas. They recommended less emphasis on rural/urban comparisons and further study of the uneven nature of rural community-based services.

Financial ability or reimbursement eligibility may greatly influence accessibility. Competitive economic pressures on agencies force them to maximize profits, often by refusing care or limiting clients served (NINR, 1994). The very oldest rural populations may include persons not eligible for Medicare or other programs, and in rural poverty areas or places with services not locally owned, the latter problem of limiting care is a potentially growing issue. Nyman and colleagues discovered that heavy use of Medicare reimbursement of rural home care for older adults sometimes limited care to postacute and rehabilitation diagnoses. They further proposed that decreased utilization of home care by this population is not necessarily due to access problems alone, but rather reflects a variety of issues such as distribution of care providers, availability of informal caregivers, reimbursement mechanisms, and patient preferences (Nyman, Sen, Chan, & Commins, 1991).

Gould and colleagues (1992) raised an important issue related to access: Should home care services be assured for all patients? Limited personnel and management capabilities in rural areas may indicate a need to reexamine policy around appropriateness of care. At present, public health nurses or county nurses provide home care coverage and case management for many isolated rural elders. The services offered are often limited to weekday daytime hours, limiting highly technical care such as ventilators, intravenous antibiotics or chemotherapy (Magilvy et al., 1994, Congdon & Magilvy, 1995). For people in areas with few private agencies or limited public health nursing, conversion or expansion of rural hospitals and nursing homes to deliver home care might be an answer, especially if such services can be moved out of the medical model into a nursing or social services approach. While this solution might also promote more local ownership and management of HCBS, some counties in the United States have neither hospitals nor nursing homes and lack public health nurse availability.

Limited research exists about accessibility of HCBS in rural areas and the absence of descriptions of exemplary modes of care is a weakness in the literature. Further, in general, rural research is limited and a series of design problems—including the prevalence of cross-sectional studies, small sample sizes and other sampling issues, and differing definitions of rurality—either weaken the knowledge base or preclude comparisons and generalizability (Weinert & Burman, 1994).

Research priorities
Exciting research opportunities and priorities related to accessibility of rural home- and community-based services have been identified by several sources, including a recent panel of experts convened by the NINR (1995); Kenney (1993); Magilvy et al. (1994), and Rowles, Beaulieu, and Myers (1995).

First, research is needed on how rural communities can develop and tailor services to their unique rural culture and limited available resources. Especially needed are studies of emerging models of locally owned or managed programs such as public health nursing care, hospital, clinic, or nursing-home-based home care services, and rural hospice services. For example, in one community in rural Colorado, the hospital, a nursing home, a home care agency, and numerous community members, clergy, and volunteer health professionals are working cooperatively to initiate a community hospice program. No hospice services are available in that six-county area. This program will meet a great need and is community-based and initiated. Program development and evaluation activities in one rural area would be strengthened by knowledge of creative solutions applied in other regions.

Second, a need is indicated for study of factors related to access and provision of care. For example, research is needed on the extent to which rural elders live outside agency catchment areas and how accessibility of HCBS for these individuals could be improved. In addition, the invisibility of services or programs in rural areas limits awareness by residents and care providers. Studies are needed on how to increase visibility so utilization is increased. Related to visibility, the consequences of limited availability of rehabilitation, mental health, social services, hospice, and adult day care are unknown.

Third, research is needed on the consequences of access problems on the complex and sometimes fragile health and health care needs of rural elders, especially the very oldest individuals. Related to these issues, the effects of delayed hospital discharge, substitution of nursing home beds for home care, or the use of hospital swing beds, adult day care, or other services in place of home care is also in need of further research (Kenney & Dubay, 1992; Nelson, 1994). Likewise, health care transitions from institutional to home- and community-based care is an area in need of further study. These issues will take on increasing importance as the population ages and health care system changes bring more of these complex cases into the community setting for care (Kenney, 1993; NINR, 1994).

Finally, considering the high degree to which care of rural elders is provided or managed by family and informal services, research is needed on the ways in which rural communities can support family care while ensuring access to appropriate assistance for those for whom this informal support is unavailable. Limited research exists on the low level of use of community and home care services by families caring for a multiproblem, complex diagnosis, or very frail elders. In concluding this section, it must be noted that all of the issues and research priorities related to accessibility discussed above have implications for policy responses and cost allocations for rural home care services.

Cost, Reimbursement, Structure, and Organizational Issues

Comparative costs of home care relative to nursing home residence are variable, but point in the direction of home care being as costly or more expensive than institutional care (Gould et al., 1992). However, of great significance to the discussion are several factors influencing how costs are determined: patient level of dependence and chronicity; actual cost of services; availability of informal support; cost of the institutional alternative; whose costs are counted (e.g., Medicare vs. Medicaid), structure and organization of care, and inclusion of real family caregiving and support costs (Gould et al., 1992). In addition, the differential reimbursement rates for rural (lower) versus urban agencies is a widely held perception by rural health professionals (Congdon & Magilvy, 1995). These issues are not well studied for rural populations. It would be helpful to be able to identify groups of individuals for whom cost differentials exist as well as to examine the situation from the perspective of rural home care providers and organizations.

Affordability of services to rural elders is another cost-related issue. Limited insurance or Social Security eligibility for some retired agricultural or mining workers, increased use of HMO and other capitation programs with variable levels of home care provision, and availability of home care provisions in long-term care insurance policies may all influence this variable. Inclusion of volunteer services, neighborhood, church, friends, or other community outreach assistance in the costs—or even a better description of the impact of these informal supports—would be helpful to this analysis.

Rural, like urban HCBS, struggle with complexity of care, fragmentation of services, and organizational problems (Gould et al., 1992; Nelson, 1994). Some believe that the home care industry needs to better support larger, more complex agencies targeting a broader range of client groups and meeting more complex clinical needs. This idea, while noteworthy, may be very difficult to implement in rural settings with lower population densities, longer distances, fewer hospitals, fewer home care agencies, fewer health care professionals, and higher costs (these problems are magnified in rural western states with highly dispersed populations of elders).

One factor that would increase success is more effective integration of services and communication among a variety of health care services in rural communities. Physician involvement in integration of services is essential; however, HCBS should not be dependent upon physician leadership, especially because little incentive exists for physicians to be involved in HCBS. Limited numbers and distribution of rural physicians, the high cost of physician time in ordering and assuming some responsibility for nonmedical care, and the nonmedical, health, social, low tech, or hospice nature of many HCBS point to the need for other models of administration, such as expansion of public health or community nursing models already in place. In addition, the heavy paperwork burden in home care is felt by nurses and physicians alike, and may be driving some professionals from practice, according to research by Congdon and Magilvy (1995). Of major importance, especially in rural areas with fewer available services, is an attitude of noncompetitive cooperation among all community professionals and paraprofessionals. Current research is lacking in these areas.

Research priorities
Research is needed on the appropriateness, acceptability, and utilization of home care services by specific groups of underserved rural elders, and the cost implications of matching services to patient needs of differing levels of complexity (NINR, 1994). The balance between cost of care and quality also needs to be examined for both medically focused and social home care, especially in isolated rural areas where services are often much more costly to provide and where distance, environment, and demographic variables impinge upon delivery of HCBS. However, home- and community-based services often have high potential to boost local economies by providing employment to local residents. These factors should be considered in developing and evaluating integrated HCBS.

Effectiveness of home care services and costs related to client outcomes is another area in urgent need of research. How health care reform measures currently being implemented in a variety of states (e.g., capitated managed care for indigent populations) will affect the determination of costs and the availability of reimbursements is anyone's guess; evaluation studies must be in place simultaneously with the implementation of reform. Rural communities need flexible reimbursement mechanisms not based upon urban models. Reimbursement issues are likely to differ across regions, states, and local cultural situations; therefore direct transfer of urban policies is inappropriate and further study is indicated. In sum, a need is indicated for comprehensive multivariate research models that explore a range of variables influencing the

organization, structure, and cost of rural HCBS; target populations; cross-rural comparisons; and work force issues (Benjamin,
1992; Nelson, 1994; Weinert & Burman, 1994).

Quality of Care

Determination of quality indicators for home care is difficult, due
to different definitions, limited outcome measures, and a need to
balance the interests of different parties such as the government,
family members, agency administrators, and staff (Gould et al.,
1992). Quality is sometimes measured by quantifiable process
indicators alone, such as numbers of clients served or length of
stay. Interactional indicators such as patient/staff relationships,
quality of family life, or changes in perceived isolation or functional status might be better indicators of high-quality rural home
care, especially from the patient or family perspective.

Although the Health Care Financing Administration (HCFA)
and other federal and insurance payers, and the Joint Commission
on Accreditation of Healthcare Organizations (JCAHO) accreditation processes for hospital-based agencies have responsibility for
ensuring quality, evaluation is inconsistent and more consumer
involvement is needed (NINR, 1994). Shaughnessy and colleagues
have conducted several studies of home care quality indicators
and are continuing to work toward reducing the number of potential indicators to a manageable level (P. Shaughnessy, personal
communication, 1994). In addition, many state and national home
care associations are developing quality measures for their con-
stituent organizations.

Research priorities
More research and evaluation studies of successful home care are
needed, and are dependent upon good process and outcome definitions and measures, grounded in an understanding of patient
and family quality of life. Redford and Severns (1994), and NINR
(1994) list several components of successful rural home care programs, including assessment and service planning, strategies for

follow-up and plan revision, client-provider partnerships in planning and providing services, ongoing quality assurance and quality improvement programs, integration of acute and chronic care services, adequately and appropriately trained staff, adequate salaries, agency financial viability, and leadership.

Research is needed to describe and predict the relationships between case mix, characteristics or culture of local rural communities, client characteristics (e.g., ethnicity, short-term, posthospital vs. chronic or terminal care needs, age, frailty, cognitive impairment) and outcomes of home care. Also related to quality and in need of study are the ways in which home- and community-based services are integrated in rural communities. For example, in some rural communities, the home care services are run from the local nursing home, which may also provide home-delivered meals, respite services, and hospice care. In another community, home care nurses make visits at the senior center or adult day care facility. Outcomes research, especially client-based outcomes and study of the effectiveness and appropriateness of HCBS for particular rural clients and communities has been strongly indicated as a need by NIH (NINR, 1994, 1995).

Coordination of Care and Transitions

Community-based long-term care includes handling and facilitating rural older adults and families in numerous care situations and transitions. In this discussion, *care transitions* are defined as movements of an older client or patient from one type or level of care to another, from one institution or agency to another, or from one functional level to another. Chronically ill elders make numerous moves to and from home, hospital, nursing home, or respite care facilities. Home care services can buffer the effects of these moves and possibly decrease costs of unnecessary hospitalization when problems can be managed at home (Magilvy et al., 1994). Short term care and diversity of caseload demographics can tax the abilities of home care agencies to meet client needs. Better integration of transitions from short-term to long-term home care is required (Gould et al., 1992; Kane & Kane, 1989).

Magilvy and colleagues, in a current study, have found that use of emergency department care in substitution for primary care is a growing problem in rural communities with poor physician coverage. Lack of discharge planning from emergency department to home care can result in costly and inappropriate hospitalizations (Magilvy & Congdon, 1995). Research on this type of transition, or primary care to home care transitions in general, is needed.

Continuity of care and coordination, monitoring, and supporting clients and families through periods of transition as well as stability in community-based long-term care are essential to smooth home care delivery. Smooth transitions and coordinated care can facilitate quality of life and help prevent premature functional decline or disability (NINR, 1994). They require, however, the use of multidisciplinary collaborative services. In addition, rural families might, in the future, be taught to be case managers (NINR, 1995). Innovative programs must be developed to fit with rural culture and needs. For example, Lee (1993) proposed that rural communities develop coordinated services linking existing community resources and providers and targeting residents across the lifespan to increase continuity and decrease duplication of services, an important factor when resources are scarce as in many rural areas.

One program in need of further research in rural areas is case management. Parker and colleagues (1992a,b) identified numerous problems in rural case management, including the effect of rural values of independence; financial and delivery system constraints, and limitations on availability and staffing. Rural case management was found to be inconsistent across settings even within the same region. Even definitions and indications for case management services differed, indicating a need for further research of this potentially valuable service modality.

Research priorities

More research is needed on care transitions and coordination or management of care (Lee, 1993; Magilvy et al., 1994; Magilvy & Congdon, 1995; NINR, 1994). Research priorities include developing an understanding of how case management and other transitional care interventions might prevent functional loss, disability, unnecessary hospitalization, or emergency room use for rural elders. Outcomes of rural case management and continuity of care should be explored and differences in nursing and social-work models identified. Research is also needed on strategies of care coordination to meet needs of patients experiencing long-term chronic or terminal illness (examining across illness episodes and treatment settings). Related to this issue is a need for research on the availability and effectiveness of rural discharge planning and planning of patient discharges from urban settings to rural homes. Limited research exists on patient, family, and care provider decision making at these critical transition points. Finally, research has been suggested on the use of technologies for communication in care management (NINR, 1994, 1995). In conclusion, in rural settings, the variable availability of HCBS, case management, informal and family caregiving support, and rural cultural variables indicate a need for development and testing of locally relevant models of case management.

Integration of Home- and Community-Based Services

Home care is not delivered in isolation. Throughout this chapter, I have considered the complex and multifaceted nature of providing care to frail, acutely, chronically, or terminally ill older adults in rural settings. The home and community serve as context for community-based long-term care services. Rural culture, ethnic diversity, aging in place, and availability of family, friends, and neighbors to assist with informal care services, all contribute to successful process and outcomes of formal health and social services. To plan and develop HCBS, a community partnership is essential. It must include community, professional, and lay leadership, strong community needs assessment, community development activities, and strategic planning leading to communication of common concerns and goals (Lee, 1993; Nelson, 1994, NINR,

1994, 1995; Redford & Severns, 1994). In the near future, we may see rural hospitals, community health centers, nursing homes, and community voluntary agencies involved in collaborating to achieve community goals for long-term care (Nelson, 1994; Redford & Severns, 1994).

Community-based services complement and support in-home services; they do not substitute for institutionalization, although this possibility may exist for some clients. Rural communities are known for good informal support, professional networks, and community partnerships; however, diversity and availability of volunteer, lay, and professional services may be limited and the best structures for linkages are not known (Hassinger, Hicks, & Godino, 1993). Little research exists to test policies that permit or exclude reimbursement or support of family caregiving activities that assist in the prevention or delay of institutionalization.

Voluntary agencies and individual community volunteers hold excellent potential for involvement with community-based long-term care clients and families. Churches, schools, community volunteer programs (e.g., Mennonite or Catholic community volunteers), peer counselors, and neighbors may all serve in various ways to close gaps in care left by out-migration of the adult children of frail elders and limitations in health and social services in some rural communities. Little research exists in this area. Using and linking existing structures and services, voluntary, lay, and professional, informal and formal, can increase accessibility, communication, and coordination of care, and decrease duplication (Lee, 1993; Magilvy et al., 1994).

In contrast to some urban programs that tend to be categorical, rural programs may be broad and often target a large population of diverse age, gender, ethnic/cultural characteristics across rural farm and nonfarm settings. It is imperative that rural health care providers work to help educate their legislators and policymakers on the diversity of HCBS options and resources available in rural areas. Policymakers should be encouraged to support flexibility in funding and strengthen programs that enhance the long-term care of older rural residents with complex health problems and care demands.

Research priorities

Research is needed to explore diverse formal care services such as hospice, rehabilitation care, adult day care, and the involvement of hospitals, nursing homes, and community health centers in provision of rural long-term HCBS. Research on the integration of mental health services with acute and chronic health care is also needed; research on mental health services for rural elders is very limited and evidence exists that integration of mental and physical health and social services is severely lacking.

Development of measures to evaluate rural community-based interventions is needed, especially measures of health outcomes, cost, and direct benefits to clients and family (NINR, 1994). Measures developed must take into account rural heterogeneity and variations in culture, population, and distribution of services and providers. The role that support networks and alternatives to traditional health care services play in decreasing hospitalization or institutionalization is in need of study (Hassinger et al., 1993). Research can also identify types of rural settings, which community services are essential to each other, and to whom they should be targeted.

Finally, the characteristics, choices, and decision-making potential of older rural residents, their families, and care providers must be taken into account in any research conducted. For example, to what extent can rural residents be involved in decision making about the balance between formal and informal rural long-term care services offered? What factors influence the choices rural residents make to obtain care either inside or external to their community? The degree to which care is culturally congruent and acceptable to rural elders, especially those of differing ethnic and cultural group, is a rich area for research and one that certainly influences utilization and cost of services.

In conclusion, integrated rural home- and community-based long-term care services is an area in need of concentrated research. Exemplary programs should be developed, evaluated, and described in the literature to examine access, cost, quality, and choice issues. Policy changes to permit development, funding, and continuation of successful programs must be considered. The characteristics of successful programs and implications for health and quality-of-life outcomes is essential knowledge in need of study and dissemination.

CONCLUSIONS

The issues discussed in this chapter on home- and community-based long-term care services for rural elders indicate a crucial need for further research and policy change. Several policy implications were noted:

1. Case mix and geographically different and flexible reimbursement for home care may be needed.

2. Support for alternative models of community-based care, adapted to heterogeneous local area needs is indicated.

3. Policy support is essential for integration of informal, family, and formal systems of care.

4. Increased outcomes research will have future policy implications.

5. Community-based care policy for rural elders must consider the long-term nature of care in a variety of care settings.

Input from rural residents, elders and health professionals, must be considered. Integration of rural HCBS with community partnerships can lead to preferred outcomes such as continuity across transitions, a balance of formal and informal care services, and long-term care congruent with local rural needs, resources, values, and culture. Such integration will facilitate the ability of even the most frail rural elders to live at their highest levels of independence and quality of life.

REFERENCES

Benjamin, A. F. (1992). An overview of in-home health and supportive services for older persons. In M. G. Ory & A. P. Duncker (Eds.),

In-home care for older people, health and supportive services (pp. 9–52). Newbury Park, CA: Sage.

Burman, M., Steeffes, M., & Weinert, C. (1994). Cancer care in Montana. *Home Health Care Services Quarterly, 14*(2/3), 37–52.

Congdon, J. G., & Magilvy, J. K. (1995). The changing spirit of rural community nursing: Documentation burden. *Public Health Nursing, 12*(1), 18–24.

Coward, R. T., Bull, C. N., Kukulka, G., & Galliher, J. M. (Eds.) (1994). *Health services for rural elders.* New York: Springer Publishing Co.

Gould, D. A., Haslanger, K. D., & Vladeck, B. C. (1992). Coming of age: Home care in the 1990s. *Pride Institute Journal of Long Term Home Health Care, 11*(1), 19–28.

Hassinger, E. W., Hicks, L. L., & Godino, V. (1993). A literature review of health issues of the rural elderly. *The Journal of Rural Health. 9,* 68–75.

Hughes, S. L. (1992). Homecare: Where we are and where we need to go. In M. G. Ory & A. P. Duncker (Eds.), *In home care for older people: Health and supportive services* (pp. 53–74). London: Sage.

Kane, R. L., & Kane, R. A. (1989). Transitions in long term care. In M. G. Ory & K. Bond (Eds.), *Aging and health care* (pp. 217–243). New York: Routledge.

Kenney, G. M. (1993). Is access to home health care a problem in rural areas? *American Journal of Public Health, 83,* 412–414.

Kenney, G. M., & Dubay, L. C. (1992). Explaining area variation in the use of Medicare home health services. *Medical Care, 30*(1), 43–57.

Krout, J. A. (Ed.) (1994). *Providing community-based services to the rural elderly.* Thousand Oaks, CA: Sage.

Lee, H. J. (1993). Rural elderly individuals: Strategies for delivery of nursing care. *Nursing Clinics of North America, 28*(1), 219–230.

Magilvy, J. K., Congdon, J. G., & Martinez, R. (1994). Circles of care: Home and community support for rural older adults. *Advances in Nursing Science, 16*(3), 22–33.

Magilvy, J. K., & Congdon, J. G. (1995). Interim report (NIH Grant # 2RO1 NR02006–05). Available from National Institute for Nursing Research.

National Institute of Nursing Research (NINR) (1995). *Community-based health care: Nursing strategies.* A report of an NINR Priority Expert Panel. Washington, DC: U.S. Department of Health & Human Services.

National Institute of Nursing Research (NINR) (1995). *Community-based health care: Nursing strategies.* (Report of the NINR Priority Expert Panel, NIH publication 95). Bethesda, MD: National Institute of Health.

Nelson, G. M. (1994). In-home services for rural elders. In R. T. Coward, C. N. Bull, G. Kukulka, & J. M. Galliher (Eds.), *Health services for rural elders* (pp. 65–83). New York: Springer Publishing Co.

Nyman, J. A., Sen, A., Chan, B. Y., & Commins, P. P. (1991). Urban/rural differences in home health patients and services. *The Gerontologist, 31,* 457–466.

Ory, M. G., & Duncker, A. P. (Eds.). (1992). *In-home care for older people, health and supportive services.* Newbury Park, CA: Sage.

Parker, M., Quinn, J., Viehl, M., McKinley, A., Polich, C. L., Detzner, D., Hartwell, S., & Korn, K. (1992). Case management in rural areas: Definition, clients, financing, staffing, and service delivery issues. *Journal of Nursing Administration, 22*(2), 54–59.

Parker, M., Quinn, J., Viehl, M., McKinley, A. H., Polich, C. L., Hartwell, S., Van Hook, R., & Detzner, D. F. (1992). Issues in rural case management. *Family and Community Health, 14*(4), 40–60.

Redford, L. J., & Severns, A. B. (1994). Home health services in rural America. In J. A. Krout, (Ed.), *Providing community based services to the rural elderly* (pp. 221–242). Thousand Oaks, CA: Sage.

Rowles, G. D., Beaulieu, J. E., & Myers, W. W. (1995). *Contemporary directions in long-term care for the rural elderly* (position paper). Lexington, KY: Sanders-Brown Center on Aging, University of Kentucky.

Salmon, M. A. P., Nelson, G. W., & Rous, S. G. (1993). The continuum of care revisited: A rural perspective. *The Gerontologist, 33,* 658–666.

Weinert, C., & Burman, M. (1994). Rural health and health-seeking behaviors. In J. J. Fitzpatrick & J. S. Stevenson (Eds.). *Annual review of nursing research* (pp. 65–92). New York: Springer Publishing Co.

Weinert, C., & Long, K. A. (1993). Support systems for the spouses of chronically ill persons in rural areas. *Family and Community Health,*

16(1), 46–54.

Zawadski R. T., & Eng, C. (1988). Case management in capitative long-term care. *Health Care Financing Review.* (Annual Suppl.), 75–81

The Role of Senior Centers in Rural Long-Term Care

5

John A. Krout

This chapter examines the roles and potential roles senior centers play in the rural long-term care continuum. A senior center is not a service like nursing care, adult day care, or physical therapy, but an organization and place where a wide range of services are either provided, arranged for directly, or facilitated through information or referral to other service providers. As a site for congregate programs, senior centers provide important opportunities for socialization and social and community integration. Senior centers function as a meeting place for seniors, a place where they can feel a sense of "belonging" and "ownership." However, considerable gaps exist in our knowledge of specific senior center programming activities and program impacts. Indeed, there is a general dearth of research on senior centers, very little study of rural senior centers and even less information on the roles played by rural senior centers in long-term care (Krout, 1989a).

The definition of long-term care is crucial to consideration of this topic. Over the years, most funding received by senior centers has been for recreational, educational, and supportive health and social services (e.g., transportation, congregate meals). Health and wellness education and promotion have received increasing attention as have programs aimed at attracting the newly retired, or "young-old." Concomitantly, many senior centers have become involved in providing services and programs to frail older persons in response to the growing numbers of impaired older persons in the community. If one defines long-term care narrowly as services directed to older persons in the community with illness and disability that limit independent functioning, then the role of senior centers in long-term care is somewhat circumscribed. If one defines long-term care as services or experiences "provided to individuals and their families for the purpose of promoting or restoring health or minimizing the effects of illness and disability" (Miller, 1991, p.17), then senior centers have made important and continuing contributions to the long-term care continuum.

Some gerontologists see senior centers as peripheral to long-term care. For example, Kane and Kane (1987) note that senior centers cannot be considered long-term care providers because so few of their participants are functionally impaired. This view is reflected by an absence of references to senior centers in most discussions of long-term care. (See Sherman [1993] for a recent exception.)

SENIOR CENTERS IN AMERICA

The modern day senior center traces its roots back to the early 1940s, when one of the earliest centers (the Hodson Center in New York City) focused on meeting the needs of low-income older people (Gelfand, 1990). Since that time, the number of senior centers has grown to between 10,000 and 15,000, depending on the definition employed (Krout, 1989a). Three White House Conferences on Aging, passage of the Older Americans Act in 1965 and subsequent amendments, and the activities of national education and advocacy organizations such as the National Council on the Aging have played important roles in this growth and expansion (Wagener, 1981). Although a number of definitions for senior centers can be found in the literature (Krout, 1989a), one of the most comprehensive is provided by the National Council on the Aging's National Institute of Senior Centers (1991):

A senior center is a community focal point on aging where older adults come together for services and activities that reflect their experience and skills, respond to their diverse needs and interests, enhance their dignity, support their independence and encourage involvement in and with the community. As part of a comprehensive community strategy to meet the needs of older adults, senior centers offer services and activities within the center and link participants with resources offered by other agencies. Center programs consist of a variety of individual and group services and activities. The center also serves as a resource for the entire community for information on aging; support for family caregivers; training professional and lay leaders and students; and for development of innovative approaches to addressing aging issues.

Many senior centers are multipurpose; they provide a wide range of health, social, recreational, and educational services (Krout, 1985). The Older Americans Act targeted senior centers to serve as community "focal points" for comprehensive service coordination and delivery at the local level (Krout, 1986, 1989a; Wagener, 1981). Traditionally, senior centers have played a key role in providing information and referral to other services in the community. The majority of elderly persons in a community are aware of and know the location of such centers (Krout, 1984; Harris & Associates, 1975).

A review of senior center research emphasizes that high levels of general senior center awareness or recognition does not mean that older persons (or service professionals in the community) know what senior centers do (Krout, 1989b). Indeed, one study found that while most of the elderly surveyed in a small urban community knew of the existence of the local senior center, few of them could identify specific services available there (Krout, 1984). I am not aware of any published research examining rural-urban differences in knowledge related to senior centers and their activities. Similarly, I am unaware of research on residential differences in the perceptions or acceptance of senior centers among the elderly. Several studies (Harris et al., 1975; Krout, 1983b) have found perceptions of senior centers to be generally positive.

Data from a 1984 national study focused on health and social situations of the elderly revealed that 13.7% of persons 60 or over had attended a senior center in the preceding year and 8% had eaten hot meals there. These percentages are much higher than those reported for other community-based services (Krout, Cutler, &

Coward, 1990). Other studies indicate that between 10% and 20% of the elderly in the United States participate in senior center activities (Harris et al., 1975; Krout, 1989a). A 10% to 20% figure translates into between 2.6 and 5.3 million people aged 65 and over. This figure should probably be increased by 1 to 1.5 million to include an additional 10% or more of the almost 11 million persons aged 60 to 64.

All of these observations suggest that senior centers are appropriate sites for the delivery of some long-term care services. In addition, they suggest that senior centers could play significant roles in the planning, coordination, and networking of services and in education and referral functions for elders, family caregivers and health/social services providers.

SENIOR CENTER ACTIVITIES AND THEIR RELATIONSHIP TO LONG-TERM CARE

Senior center programming has grown considerably since the 1970s. Indeed, senior centers in America today offer a large number and wide range of activities and services. Data from a recent national survey of over 400 senior centers indicate that senior centers offer an average of 16 services and 11 activities (Krout, 1990a). Examples include transportation, health and nutrition, in-home services, counseling, information and referral, education, leadership, volunteer opportunities, and recreation. Ninety percent of senior centers were reported to offer information and referral, transportation, and congregate meal services and 70% offered home-delivered meals. Three quarters of the centers offered health screening and maintenance, health education, and nutrition education. Information and assistance services (housing; crime prevention; financial, tax, and legal assistance; and social security) were offered by two thirds of centers while one half reported providing information on welfare programs. A smaller percentage of the centers reported that they provided in-home services. Three fifths indicated that they provided telephone reassurance and friendly visiting but only 30% offered homemaker, home health, and home repair/winterization. Special services, income supplement, and personal counseling and mental health services were offered by an even smaller percentage of centers (between 20% and 40%). In addition, 10% offered vision and hearing services, 15% offered adult day care, 23% provided protective services, and 25% conducted programs for the handicapped. All of these programs can assist impaired older persons. Such offerings include on-site programs specifically geared to the impaired, as well as services delivered to individual or group residences or provided through referral.

Not surprisingly, centers with larger budgets, more staff, affiliations with multiservice organizations and with a larger proportion of older users with higher incomes reported more programs (Krout, 1990a). Rural senior centers offered fewer activities and services than urban centers, about 20% fewer on average. Considerable variation was found within the urban and rural groups. Most of the rural centers offered the same core services of transportation, information and referral and health promotion and education as the urban centers and many offered programs of particular value to impaired elders (Krout, 1990a).

As noted in the introduction to this chapter, the significance and appropriateness of senior centers as a part of the long-term care continuum is a subject of some disagreement. Many researchers examining center participation and participants have observed that impaired older persons are often underserved (Hanssen et al., 1978; Leanse & Wagner, 1975; Monk, 1988; Ralston, 1987), and that older individuals who are physically and mentally impaired make up a very small percentage of senior center users (Krout, 1989a). Hanssen et al. (1978) observed that senior center programming does not consistently address the needs of older persons with physical limitations or mental health problems. On the other hand, research also suggests that compared with other organizations, senior centers are significantly involved with programming for impaired older people (Conrad, Hughes, Campione, & Goldberg, 1988; Jacobs, 1980).

Conrad et al. (1988) reported on a 1986 nationwide study of 1,200 adult day care centers and noted that senior centers were the fourth most often cited referral source for freestanding adult day care programs. Senior centers were also found to be the most frequent co-location site for nonfreestanding adult day care programs. One in seven of the adult day care programs reported sharing a site with a senior center and 17% with a nutrition program. These data indicate that senior centers play an important role in serving physically and cognitively impaired older adults.

A mid-1980s survey of Maryland senior centers found that almost half served the visually handicapped, one third the hearing impaired, and almost two thirds the mobility impaired (Maryland Association of Senior Centers, 1984). An earlier study of the senior center role in serving frail or at-risk older people was conducted by the National Institute of Senior Centers (Jacobs, 1980). Data from 159 centers in Maryland revealed that, despite severe funding limitations, 84% attempted to serve at-risk older persons. Most of these centers coordinated their efforts with other community agencies.

Few studies have focused specifically on senior center programming for impaired older persons. A 1993 search of the *Ageline* database (AARP, n.d.) identified only 25 articles and papers on senior center programming for at-risk older people, although a number of other studies provided data relevant to this topic. The studies focused on a variety of programming activities and covered areas such as wellness education and health promotion, health care clinics, the transition from hospitals and nursing homes to independent living, adult day care, developmental disabilities, mental health, and sensory impairments. In most cases, the programs were not rural.

UTILIZATION OF SENIOR CENTERS BY IMPAIRED OLDER PERSONS

Historically, senior centers have not focused their attention on any one group, because the senior center movement is based on the idea that all older people can benefit and contribute to this form of social organization. Similarly, the lack of specific reference to impaired older persons may reflect a philosophy that focuses on the strengths of older persons and not their weaknesses.

Current data on senior center programming and participation

suggest that many senior centers devote considerable attention to the healthy older person (Krout, 1989a). Most research suggests that senior center users generally have higher levels of health, social interaction, and life satisfaction and lower levels of income than nonusers (Krout, 1989a; Krout et al., 1990). Data on user versus nonuser differences in gender, race, marital status, and education are less specific.

Some individuals in need of long-term care are much more likely to participate in senior centers than others; and some senior centers—because of their location in communities with large numbers of low-income, minority, and very old persons—serve larger numbers of impaired individuals. Yet, as senior center user populations "age in place" and as young-old participants choose activities outside of senior centers, these organizations face increasing numbers of physically and mentally impaired participants in need of supportive programming.

Nationwide, the data suggest that 5% to 10% of the older persons attending senior centers are vision or hearing impaired, frail in health, or cognitively impaired. Older people with physical and mental impairments are less likely to attend a senior center than their healthier counterparts—by a ratio of between 3 and 5 to 1 (Krout, 1989a). A recent California study comparing the use of services by individuals with Alzheimer's disease who live alone with those who live with someone found that 10.5% of the former and 8.1% of the latter group reported attending a senior center (Webber Fox, & Burnette, 1994). The study did not report on the place of residence of the participants.

While one cannot say with certainty how many persons in need of long-term care services attend senior centers and receive appropriate services, data suggest that the senior center population is getting older and more impaired. Thus, senior centers are likely to provide services to a segment of the long-term care population. A recent national survey of over 400 senior centers found the following participant characteristics: 11% under 65; 41% between the ages of 65 and 74; 37% aged 75 to 84; and 10% aged 85 and over. Seventy-five percent were female, 71% were unmarried, and 85% were Caucasian. Slightly more than 25% reported incomes of less than $5,000, 36% incomes from $5,000 to $9,999, and 37% had incomes greater than $10,000 (Krout, 1990a). When these figures are compared to data collected from the same sample in 1982, the main change is that the center participants are older. Older average ages were reported by 56% of respondents; only 14% reported younger participants. Respondents were about equally split when it came to changes in the reported health of participants. Three out of 10 indicated that participants' health had declined while 27% reported improved health. Approximately 60% reported an increase in the number of participants categorized as frail, while 12% indicated a decrease. As senior center user populations age and become more impaired, senior centers will increasingly serve elders in need of long-term care services.

SENIOR CENTER LINKAGES AND LONG-TERM CARE

A primary function of senior centers is the provision of information on programs and services and appropriate referral of older persons to other agencies. Some information and referral is conducted informally through interaction with staff and other participants, but more formal linkage to community resources is also stressed. The information/referral role is an important one in the long-term care network and can be studied through an examination of senior center linkages.

In the late 1980s, a study was conducted of linkages for a national sample of 250 senior centers (Krout, 1987, 1989b). One quarter of the respondents reported that their centers worked with only a few organizations while one fifth indicated work with other organizations for most of the services that they offered. Half of the respondents indicated that most of their linkages were informal and that more formal arrangements, such as memos of understanding and contracts, were used infrequently.

Sending referrals to and receiving them from other agencies was the most common form of linkage activity, followed in frequency by service delivery planning and coordination. Organizations most likely to be involved with senior centers in the linkage process included Social Security or health departments, nutrition sites, other senior centers, county social services, visiting nurses/ home health agencies, hospitals, physicians, nursing homes, housing authorities, legal aid, religious organizations, and Area Agencies on Aging (AAAs) (Krout, 1989b). Many of these agencies are central to the provision of long-term care.

SENIOR CENTERS, FOCAL POINTS, AND LONG-TERM CARE

The Older Americans Act (1965) and its amendments helped to fuel the spread of linkages. In particular, the 1973 amendments introduced the term *focal point* and the 1978 amendments increased the attention given to the concept by explicitly outlining the role that local senior centers should play in bringing senior citizens in contact with the myriad of programs and agencies designed to meet their needs. Research by Wagener (1981) found that 66% of the organizations designated as focal points by AAAs were senior centers and 27% were nutrition sites. A more recent study found that 74% of the senior centers in a small national sample reported focal point status (Krout, 1987).

Recent interviews with a national sample of rural AAA directors revealed that programs involving staff from other agencies and organizations often utilize a senior center on a regular (but not daily) basis for varied services (Krout, 1989c). Many directors with multicounty, rural planning and service areas (PSAs) reported that senior centers act as the hub of service and information provision for seniors with access, health, and social needs. Regardless of the mix of local versus AAA funding, senior centers generally had considerable visibility and support in these communities and often served as a major entry point into the service system. Indeed, senior centers were identified more often than other organizations by AAA directors as service delivery sites (Krout, 1989c). In rural communities, the absence of other service sites and providers often leaves senior centers as the only service/information and referral point for elders.

RURAL SENIOR CENTERS

The importance of rural senior centers as sites for the provision of activities and services, information and referral, and social support has been demonstrated in the literature. Unfortunately, research focusing on the nature and impact of senior centers on the long-term care needs of impaired older persons is virtually nonexistent. Descriptions of rural senior center programming can be found, but these descriptions do not focus on specific target groups. This is unfortunate because gerontological research has consistently shown elders living in smaller communities (especially those residing in nonmetropolitan nonfarm areas) to be in need of long-term care services. Rural elders have lower incomes than urban older persons and generally have been found to be in poorer health and live in less adequate housing (Coward & Lee, 1985; Dwyer, Lee, & Coward, 1990; Krout, 1986, 1994). Also, research has shown that many rural areas have significant gaps in service availability and that rural older persons face considerable barriers in accessing existing services (Coward et al., 1994, Krout, 1986, 1994).

The lack of availability and accessibility of rural services would suggest lower utilization rates for rural senior centers. However, not all research has supported this expectation. May, Herman, and Fitzgerald (1976) uncovered no rural-urban differences for participation in a congregate meal program and Taietz (1970) found considerably higher rural senior center attendance rates in a New York State study. A recent analysis of a large national data set by Krout et al. (1990) revealed interesting differences in patterns of senior center utilization by residence. This research analyzed data from the 1984 Supplement on Aging of *the National Health Interview Survey* (National Center for Health Statistics, 1984) and found similar overall utilization rates for nonmetropolitan nonfarm residents (15%) and suburban elderly (14%), and a slightly lower rate for central city elders (12%). Elderly farm dwellers, on the other hand, recorded an 8% utilization rate. The relatively high rates for nonmetropolitan nonfarm elders may reflect the availability of senior centers and the relative absence of service alternatives. The considerably lower rates for farm dwellers may reflect availability and accessibility problems, a lack of interest in senior centers and the fact that farm elders are more likely to be married and live with a spouse than nonfarm rural elders (Coward, Bull, Kukulka, & Galliher, 1994; Krout, 1986; see also Stoller, Chapter 3 in this volume). Nonmetropolitan nonfarm older persons report higher levels of disability than nonmetropolitan farm residents.

Several national studies have focused on residential differences in senior center resources, programming, and utilization (Krout, 1983a, 1990a). The most recent research involved a longitudinal study of 424 senior centers surveyed in 1982 and again in 1989 (Krout, 1990a). Rural-urban comparisons for the data were made using a 5-point population size continuum. (Less than 2,500, 2,500–9,999, 10,000–24,999, 25,000–49,999, and 50,000 or more.)

A number of this study's findings are relevant to examination of the roles and potential roles of senior centers in rural long-term care. First, the data revealed that rural senior centers had less space, smaller budgets, and fewer staff than urban centers. Second, rural senior centers generally offered a smaller number and less range of services to fewer elders. Third, the rural centers were more likely to have experienced declines in budget and participation than urban centers. The significance of these findings must be interpreted in relation to the context of rural communities' demographics and service systems. It is not surprising that rural senior centers have smaller facilities since facility size is related to number of participants and rural communities with their smaller populations would be expected to have fewer senior center users. The average daily attendance at rural senior centers was reported to be about 50. Likewise, the smaller number of services reported by rural centers reflects the smaller number and range of services and service practitioners found in rural areas.

None of these findings provides direct evidence that rural senior centers do not and/or cannot provide important services and activities in support of the elderly's long-term care needs. Although they offer fewer services with smaller numbers of staff, rural senior centers still provide a core of services that meet at least some of the long-term care needs of rural elders. These include information and referral, nutrition, health education and promotion, socialization and, in some cases, more specialized services such as home-based care, adult day care and case management. And it is important to note that considerable variation was found in rural center activities, with some organizations offering a full array of services.

Finally, my research has found significant rural-urban differences in senior center participation characteristics. Rural center users were older, less healthy and had lower incomes. These factors have generally been found to be associated with higher levels of long-term care need. No significant community size differences were found for change in the age, percentage male or female participants, and number of frail elders. It should be noted that an increase in the number of frail elders may be having greater impact on rural centers (Krout, 1990a). Thus, it could be argued that rural senior center users, overall, fit the profile of the long-term care population better than do urban center users.

RURAL SENIOR CENTERS AND LONG-TERM CARE FOR IMPAIRED OLDER PERSONS

Several factors should be kept in mind when considering appropriate roles for senior centers in rural long-term care. One is the demography of rural areas— specifically, population size and density. Often viewed as central defining characteristics of rurality, small population size and low population density create access problems that limit the effectiveness and appropriateness of large, centralized service systems and make it difficult to achieve significant economies of scale. Rural senior centers, with their roots in local communities and cultures, are, however, in a position to be sensitive and responsive to the needs of older persons. They can be more easily accessed than service sites in larger but more distant communities. A second factor is culture. As has been stated by a number of gerontologists (Coward & Lee, 1985; Krout, 1988; Rowles, 1988), rural social and cultural systems differ from urban ones as well as from each other. Thus, urban-based long-term care models must be "ruralized" in order to become appropriate for rural populations. Finally, rural informal and formal support networks have characteristics that long-term care services must reflect. For example, rural service systems are often less fully developed and lack financial, material and human resources (Coward & Lee, 1985; Krout 1986, 1994). This does not mean that solutions to at least some of the long-term care needs of rural older persons cannot be found. It means that they may be best met in unique and varied ways. Rural service professionals need the autonomy and resources to develop responses that work in individual communities.

In this context, what are appropriate long-term care roles for rural senior centers? I have noted that senior centers can and do play significant community focal point roles, partly because rural communities often have few other organizations that can carry out such functions. Distance to services in urban centers creates transportation difficulties and, in addition, rural older persons may not be comfortable leaving their community to obtain services in an unfamiliar place from professionals who know little of their background. Rural senior centers can develop a focal role and serve as a point of access for long-term care services based in other (i.e., larger) communities.

Because of their visibility, rural senior centers in extremely low population density areas can serve as a base for in-home services as well as outreach services such as guardianship, "friendly visitors," and medical transportation. The community roots and familiarity of senior center staff with local needs, populations, community values, and lifestyles are an important asset in identifying and bringing isolated older persons into the system. Senior centers in larger rural communities can serve as a hub for a network of long-term care services through linkages with nutrition sites, senior clubs, church and farm groups, and other community organizations.

Several examples serve to illustrate these types of roles. Wyoming (a "frontier" rural state) has developed a community-based, case-managed, in-home services program administered under the auspices of senior centers. Throughout the state, paraprofessionals located in multipurpose senior centers serve as case managers for frail older persons (Miller & Auker, 1991). Other examples of the involvement of rural senior centers in long-term care include (Krout, 1990b):

- social and medical model adult day care co-located with senior centers;

- center staff training to detect elder abuse;

- exercise programs and health education for older persons with physical impairments;

- caregiver support and counseling;

- case management programs;

- integration of handicapped elders in center programming;

- mental health counseling at centers;

- mobile health screening;

- geriatric assessment by medical staff.

Data indicate that the characteristics of older populations and senior center users (and hence resource and programming needs) differ by community size. The major rural-urban differences (as indicated by the data presented in this chapter) are in the areas of age, income, and health. Rural older persons appear to be in greater need of an array of programs that senior centers can either provide or can facilitate through education and referral. Such activities include income support (e.g., SSI, food stamps, heating assistance, opportunities to supplement incomes); health and wellness education and promotion (e.g. nutrition, exercise, stress reduction); a variety of health screening activities (dental, blood pressure, vision, hearing, diabetes, etc.) and health maintenance and rehabilitative services.

Unfortunately, many program needs are less likely to be adequately met in rural areas because senior centers and the aging services network in general lack the dollars and health service professionals to provide them. This does not mean that such needs are impossible to meet, only that they are more difficult. Training and resource materials can and should be developed to build the capacity of senior centers to meet the long-term care needs of rural elders. Traditional linkages with other agencies and the adoption of existing communication technologies (e.g., remote broadcast and videos) can also serve to overcome resource gaps and accessibility problems.

Another important issue is how well prepared rural senior centers are to accommodate impaired older people. Planning is essential and the need for greater planning for impaired older persons is noted by both Monk (1988) and Jacobs (1980). Lack of financial resources, space, and staff training are often cited as other barriers to senior centers' accommodation of impaired older people. For example, three fifths of the directors in Monk's study of a sample of New York State senior centers reported the need for more money to facilitate the utilization of their centers by impaired older people. Center directors surveyed by Jacobs (1980) reported a similar concern, even though 40% said they received special funds for programs for impaired older people. Lack of time was also identified by center directors as restricting their work with this population.

In addition to money, staff training is essential to enable rural senior centers to incorporate larger numbers of impaired older people into existing programs or to allow centers to develop special programs for them. Only one third of the center directors in Monk's (1988) study reported staff training related to conditions of impairment and almost 90% of the sample studied by Jacobs (1980) indicated a need for staff training on the special requirements of impaired older people. Rural senior centers often have only one or two part-time professionally trained staff members with multiple responsibilities. Ideally, additional monies should be made available to hire professional staff, but where this is not feasible and volunteers must supervise and guide impaired participants, in-depth training of volunteers and paid staff becomes essential (Monk, 1988).

Some impaired elders require environmental supports. While Monk (1988) found that center directors in New York State felt their centers were well suited to accommodate impaired older people, this may not be the case in other states and in rural areas. Transportation was reported by rural service providers to be a major problem. Getting healthy rural older persons to and from senior centers is expensive and often a challenge. Transporting less functionally able elders can be particularly problematic.

Linkages with other agencies and organizations within and beyond the local community are fundamental to the successful involvement of impaired elders in senior centers. Two thirds of the center directors surveyed by Jacobs (1980) noted that knowledge of community resources and information on successful programming models was a "special need" and 94% indicated that they coordinated services with other community agencies. Monk (1988) concluded that senior centers serving impaired older people must utilize existing service networks for both diagnostic and programmatic resources. Rural centers may have to develop some of these capabilities themselves.

SUMMARY AND CONCLUSIONS

Overall, what do the data tell us about the roles played by senior centers in rural long-term care? First, rural senior centers offer a range of services without the benefit of a large number of resources. While resource limitations constrain service development and provision, they have forced rural senior centers to be creative and, one could argue, cost effective. Second, rural senior centers have participants who are older, poorer and sicker than urban ones—all characteristics related to the need for long-term care. Third, rural senior centers play important focal point roles for long-term care information and access. Finally, as senior center user populations age in place, centers are facing increasing numbers of physically and mentally impaired participants who require supportive programming. Concomitantly, the number of impaired older persons who are capable of living independently in the community with appropriate supportive services is increasing dramatically as is the need and demand for health promotion and disease prevention services. Thus, there is a demographic as well as a social imperative for more information to support rural senior center activities for impaired older populations.

Knowledge of rural senior center programs serving impaired older persons and the factors involved in their development and operation is limited. Few studies have examined those factors responsible for the variation in programming quantity, quality and impact. No research with nationally representative samples has specifically focused on the factors related to variation in rural center programming for impaired older people. Even basic information on the numbers of impaired older persons utilizing rural senior centers is unavailable. Important conceptual issues such as difficulties involved in integrating impaired older persons in senior center activities should be explored. Researchers and practitioners should begin to explore how these questions can best be investigated and resolved. Senior centers should be considered part of the rural long-term care continuum and researchers should include them as one of many alternative modes of service provision to impaired older persons.

It is clear that senior centers have grown and diversified over the years. Rural senior centers face considerable resource challenges. Yet, shifts in federal and state spending and priorities in health and social services for the elderly that focus on cost containment and targeting at-risk individuals suggest a need for rural senior centers to become more focused on providing long-term care services. In many respects, senior centers are already involved. The aging in place of their user populations as well as greater disability levels among the rural elderly in general provide both opportunity and responsibility. Against this backdrop, I offer several recommendations:

1. *Need for resources* Starting with the assumption that rural senior centers can play significant long-term care roles either through information and referral and/or direct service provision, existing reimbursement and program allocation policies should be altered to direct more resources to rural senior centers for long-term care activities. This must occur at federal, state, and local levels.

2. *Need for research* There is a large gap between what is known about the long-term care activities of rural senior centers and what should be known to make an accurate assessment of their contributions in the area of long-term care. Basic

descriptive data are lacking on the number and characteristics of impaired rural elders served by senior centers, the nature of the services that they receive, and the impact of these services on individuals. Larger systemic issues, such as service availability, accessibility, and cost, must also be assessed. Research should be conducted to determine the factors and resources that differentiate those rural centers that do and do not make significant contributions to meeting the long-term care needs of rural elders. Other research questions with important implications for policy and practice include, What aspects of long-term care cannot be carried out effectively and efficiently by senior centers? and How can senior centers best be utilized to increase access to other components of rural long-term care systems?

3. *Training and technical assistance* More resources should be devoted to providing training and technical assistance to senior centers to increase their capacity to provide long-term care services. The Administration on Aging (AoA) should provide assistance by supporting demonstration projects and training programs. The AoA-funded National Resource Center on Rural Long-Term Care should make senior centers one of its target organizations. Grants-in-aid must be made available to rural senior center staff to attend training programs, which are usually conducted in urban areas, and states should develop well-planned local guidelines that include senior centers in long-term care training and technical assistance initiatives. Demonstration projects should be supported that examine alternative models of senior center participation in rural long-term care information and service delivery.

Up to this point, I have noted factors such as training, technical assistance, planning, linkages, resource development, and research. My observations have been largely directed at incremental change and presume little, if any, change or reconceptualization of rural senior centers. While these factors are important, policymakers, practitioners, academics and older adults should examine the fundamental practices and operation of rural senior centers and their relationship to long-term care. A basic question is, How can senior centers be best utilized as a component of rural long-term care without adding resources?

One possibility is to integrate senior centers more fully into existing health and social service networks that are not focused on older adults. In some communities this is done both symbolically and operationally by locating programs for older adults in community centers that serve all persons regardless of age. Thus, adult day care and child day care are co-located in the same facility and transportation systems provide service access for elders as well as other age groups. Likewise, rural senior centers could emphasize family issues and become focal to a broad spectrum of activities designed to involve older persons in other aspects of community. Such practices could result in greater service availability for all ages as resources from multiple funding sources are used to support a wider range of on-site programs and professionals.

Another possibility is to develop a multitier model of senior centers explicitly recognizing that not every rural community can have a center that provides a wide range of services. However, this model can concentrate limited resources to the point that large areas have no senior center with the capacity to address essential long-term care needs. An alternative is a system of centers operating like a wheel with a multipurpose regional center as a hub connected to a number of smaller centers and nutrition sites. The smaller centers could support a core of socialization, recreation, and nutrition services. The hub centers would offer a full range of services including respite services, case management, employment, and perhaps even evolve into a "campus" setting providing residential options. This hub system could give senior centers a critical mass that would enhance their ability to work with other service systems such as health and social services, compete for existing resources, and coordinate a system that regularly provides specialized services to the smaller sites.

Elements of this model can already be found in a number of rural areas (Krout, Williams, & Owen, 1994), but often the smaller centers are not well integrated into the hub programmatically and care has not been taken to develop a planning process that truly involves them, which would lead to a sense of ownership in the system. Since older adults in small rural communities are often most comfortable with the intimacy of "their" center and may be reluctant to receive services elsewhere, care must be taken to acknowledge and respond appropriately to such feelings. In sum, new approaches must be instituted if rural senior centers and communities are to successfully evolve and survive.

Rural senior centers are especially vulnerable to current trends. These trends include decreased funding, rural economic decline, the aging in place of current center user populations and concomitant loss of center leadership, increasing centralization of health care services in large health care organizations, and difficulty in attracting newly retired older adults. These trends suggest that the traditional rural senior center may well find itself without public funding or the broad-based community support necessary to survive in the sunrise years of the 21st century. To avoid this fate, rural senior centers should "reinvent" themselves through examination of the fundamental roles they play in their communities. Rural hospitals and, in some cases, rural nursing homes have done this; so, too, can rural senior centers. To reinvent means to reexamine goals and objectives and the roles centers play in meeting the health and social needs of all age groups in the community. The term *senior center* (with emphasis on *senior*) may be inappropriate for the 21st century. Long-term care involves us all and is based on the interdependency and mutual support of people of all ages, whether it be provided within the family context or by formal service providers and practitioners.

One of the strengths often attributed to rural living is a sense of community and a willingness of people to help neighbors when assistance is needed. Rural senior centers have built on this characteristic in the past and should continue to do so. It is possible that the evolution of government policy toward funding by categories and discrete program areas has diluted this strength. Although they may guarantee short-term survival, rural senior centers that respond to the long-term care challenge largely by fighting for their "piece of the pie" may miss a significant opportunity to expand their role in the community and to ensure that needed long-term care options are available to old and young persons alike.

In conclusion, one of the strengths of senior centers is their diversity and their ability to serve different segments of the older population in different ways. Rural senior centers do many things well with relatively few resources and certainly are capable of improving and expanding existing functions given an appropriate mandate and resources. They are challenged by the growth of a larger and more diverse older population during times of fiscal constraints. Although a part of the community-based services system, senior centers continue to carry an image for some (elderly, policymakers, and academics alike) of places largely for recreation and socialization. It would be regrettable if the wealth of talent, energy, and dedication found in senior center professionals, volunteers, and participants were not incorporated into the rural long-term care network as we move into the 21st century.

REFERENCES

American Association of Retired Persons. (n.d.) *Ageline data base on middle age and aging,* Washington, DC: Author.

Conrad, K., Hughes, S., Campione, P., & Goldberg, R. (1988, November/December). Shedding new light on adult day care. *Perspective on Aging,* pp. 18–21.

Coward, R., & Lee, G. (1985). *The elderly in rural society.* New York: Springer Publishing Co.

Coward, R., Bull, N., Kukulka, G., & Galliher, J. (Eds.) (1994). *Health services for rural elders.* New York: Springer Publishing Co.

Dwyer, J. W., Lee, G. R., & Coward, R. T. (1990). The health status, health services utilization and support networks of the rural elderly. *Journal of Rural Health, 6,* 379–398.

Gelfand, D. (1990). *The aging services network* (2nd ed.). New York: Springer Publishing Co.

Hanssen, A., Meima, N., Buckspan, L., Henderson, B., Helbig, T., & Zarit,

S. (1978). Correlates of senior center participation. *The Gerontologist, 18,* 193–199.

Harris, L., & Associates, Inc. (1975). *The myth and reality of aging in America.* Washington, DC: The National Council on the Aging.

Jacobs, B. (1980). *Senior centers and the at-risk older person.* Washington, DC: The National Council on the Aging.

Kane, R., & Kane, R. (1987). *Long-term care.* New York: Springer Publishing Co.

Krout, J. A. (1983a). *The organization, operation, and programming of senior centers: A national survey.* Final report to the AARP (American Association of Retired Persons) Andrus Foundation. Fredonia, NY: State University of New York, Unpublished manuscript.

Krout, J. A. (1983b). Correlates of senior center utilization. *Research on Aging, 5,* 339–352.

Krout, J. A. (1984). Knowledge of senior center activities among the elderly. *Journal of Applied Gerontology, 3,* 71–81.

Krout, J. A. (1985). Senior center activities and services: Findings from a national survey. *Research on Aging, 7,* 455–471.

Krout, J. A. (1986). *The aged in rural America.* Westport, CT: Greenwood.

Krout, J. A. (1987). *Senior center linkages and the provision of services to the elderly.* Final report to the AARP Andrus Foundation. Fredonia, NY: State University of New York, Unpublished.

Krout, J. A. (1988). The elderly in rural environments. *Journal of Rural Studies, 4* (2), 103–114.

Krout, J. A. (1989a). *Senior centers in America.* Westport, CT: Greenwood.

Krout, J. A. (1989b). The nature and correlates of senior center linkages. *The Journal of Applied Gerontology. 8,* 307–322.

Krout, J. A. (1989c). *Area agencies on aging: Service planning and provision for the rural elderly.* Final report to the Retirement Research Foundation. Fredonia, NY: State University of New York; Unpublished.

Krout, J. A. (1990a). *The organization, operation, and programming of senior centers in America: A seven year follow-up.* Final report to the AARP Andrus Foundation. Fredonia, NY.

Krout, J. A. (1990b). *Meeting the needs of rural elders: Eighty program profiles.* Kansas City: National Resource Center on Rural Elderly.

Krout, J. A. (1994). (Ed.). *Providing community-based services to the rural elderly.* Thousand Oaks, CA: Sage.

Krout, J. A., Cutler, S., & Coward, R. T. (1990). Correlates of senior center participation: A national analysis. *The Gerontologist, 30,* 72–79.

Krout, J. A., Williams, M. M., & Owen, O. (1994). Senior centers in rural communities (pp. 90–113). In Krout, J. A. *Providing community-based services to the rural elderly.*Thousand Oaks, CA: Sage.

Leanse, J., & Wagner, L. (1975). *Senior centers: A report of senior group programs in America.* Washington, DC: The National Council on the Aging.

Maryland Association of Senior Centers (1984). *Report on MASC survey of senior centers.* Unpublished report.

May, A., Herman, S., & Fitzgerald, J. (1976). *An evaluation of congregate meals programs and the health of elders: Scott County and Fort Smith, Arkansas* (Bulletin No. 808). Fayetteville: University of Arkansas.

Miller, J. (1991). *Community-based long-term care: Innovative models.* Newbury Park, CA: Sage.

Miller J., & Auker, M. (1991). A social model for community-based in home services for the profoundly rural elderly. In J. Miller (Ed.), *Community-based long-term care: Innovative models* (pp. 120–129). Newbury Park, CA: Sage.

Monk, A. (1988). *The integration of frail elderly into senior centers.* Final report to the AARP Andrus Foundation. New York: Columbia University, School of Social Work, Unpublished.

National Council on the Aging. (1991). *Senior center standards: Guidelines for practice.* Washington, DC: The National Council on the Aging.

National Center for Health Statistics. (1984). *The national health interview survey design, 1973–1984, and procedures, 1975–1983.* Vital and Health Statistics Series, No. 18. Hyattsville, MD: D.S. Public Health Service.

Ralston, P. (1987). Senior center research: Policy from knowledge? In E. Borgatta & R. Montgomery (Eds.), *Critical issues in aging policy: Linking research and values*(pp.201–234). Newbury Park, CA: Sage.

Rowles, G. (1988). What's rural about rural aging? An Appalachian perspective. *Journal of Rural Studies, 4*(2), 115–124.

Sherman, R. (1993). Developing long-term care roles for America's senior centers. In J. Toner, L. Tepper, & B. Greenfield (Eds.), *Long-term care:*

Management, scope and practical issues (pp. 221–230). Philadelphia: Charles Press.

Taietz, P. (1970). *Community structure and aging.* Ithaca, NY: Cornell University Press.

Wagener, L. (1981). *The concept of a focal point for service delivery in the field of aging.* Washington, DC: The National Council on the Aging.

Webber, P., Fox, P., & Burnette, D. (1994). Living alone with Alzheimer's disease: Effects on health and social service utilization. *The Gerontologist, 34,* 8–14.

Nursing Homes in the Rural Long-Term Care Continuum

6

Graham D. Rowles

The nursing home, as we know it, is obsolete; and particularly so in rural areas. In this chapter I argue that the changing landscape of long-term care is likely to result in the emergence of new types of facilities that will not only more fully integrate rural nursing homes within the long-term care continuum and the communities within which they are located, but also will reflect patterns of care and caring that are consistent with rural life and values. Evidence presented from recent literature and from my own research will show that such a transition may already be in progress.

I first describe the emergence of the nursing home as a feature of the rural health care landscape and summarize the scant available data on the current availability of nursing home beds in rural America. This information provides the backdrop for a brief review of what is known about rural nursing homes with respect to characteristics of their residents and the care they provide. Several issues discussed provide the focus of contemporary debates on rural nursing home care and its place within the rural long-term care continuum. These issues lend support to the thesis that there is a need to reconceptualize our understanding of the role of the rural nursing home in a way that makes it possible for this institution to develop an identity more consistent with the characteristics of rural communities. A glimpse of the potential for achieving such rapprochement is provided in a case study description of Mountain View, a rural nursing home where high levels of

community integration and "permeability" have evolved naturally. Interpreting the findings from Mountain View in the context of
recent advocacy for change in the provision of rural long-term care
results in a set of key principles that provide the foundation for an
expanded view of the role of rural nursing homes. In the final section of the chapter these principles are translated into practical
suggestions to transform the rural nursing home.

It is helpful to frame this somewhat ambitious set of objectives
within the context of an interpretation of the changing role of the
nursing home in rural society. This is a difficult task because, apart
from a recent critical synthesis by Shaughnessy (1994), we know
remarkably little about rural nursing homes.

THE NURSING HOME IN RURAL SOCIETY

Historical Context

Although it has a number of historical precedents, the nursing
home is a relatively recent phenomenon that has proliferated over
the past five decades (Haber, 1983; Johnson & Grant, 1985).
Between 1939 and 1960 the U.S. Bureau of the Census reported a
rapid increase in the number of nursing homes from only 1,200
facilities nationwide with a total of 25,000 beds to 9,582 facilities
with 331,000 beds (U.S. Senate, 1974). In the following decades, in
part as a result of passage of the Older Americans Act in 1965, the
number of nursing homes continued to increase. In 1976 there
were 14,133 nursing homes with 1,291,632 beds, and by 1986 this
number had increased to 16,033 facilities with 1,615,771 beds
(National Center for Health Statistics, 1992).

While no data are available on nursing homes in rural areas
during the early phases of this rapid growth, a significant proportion
of the more recent increase in the number of facilities involves
nursing homes in rural areas. In most rural areas the arrival of
nursing homes represented a somewhat alien cultural imposition
on the landscape. Essentially, the nursing home was an incursion
within a setting that was traditionally characterized by a distinctly
noninstitutional ethos of care (Pihlblad, 1975; Salber, 1983). Many

studies of rural culture and values suggest that nursing homes were contrary to prevalent values and to a focus on family-based obligations for care within a "we take care of our own" ethos. Emphasis on independence and self-reliance as fundamental rural values was such that the nursing home came to be viewed as a last, if necessary, resort. In spite of this, somewhat paradoxically, rural nursing homes gradually evolved into key health care resources because they were in many areas the only long-term care option available. The well-documented relative lack of formal services and alternatives to institutional long-term care in rural areas (Nelson, 1980, Taietz & Milton, 1979), tended to reinforce institutionalization as the only formal long-term care option. It also provided the impetus for rural nursing homes to develop in a rather different way than their urban counterparts.

AVAILABILITY OF NURSING HOME CARE IN RURAL AREAS

Two recent studies provide critical information on the current availability of nursing home beds in rural areas (Coward, Duncan, & Uttaro, 1996; Shaughnessy, 1994). From an analysis of 1990 Medicare provider-of-service data tapes, Shaughnessy (1994) estimated that in 1990 there were 15,227 nursing homes certified by Medicare or Medicaid (the analysis omits facilities not certified by Medicaid or Medicare). Of these facilities, 6,150 (40.4%) were located in rural settings. This represented 62 certified nursing home beds per 1,000 nonmetropolitan elderly in comparison with a figure of 45 beds per 1,000 elderly for metropolitan areas. Shaughnessy's analysis also revealed that rural nursing homes tended to be smaller than those in metropolitan areas with 86% having 120 beds or less (in contrast with 65% of metropolitan nursing homes). The average number of certified "skilled nursing facility" (SNF) beds was also much lower (39 in contrast to 72) reflecting both the tendency for greater emphasis on chronic rather than acute care in many rural facilities and the inability of rural areas to attract the skilled nursing personnel (physical, speech, and occupational therapists) who would enable them to become certified for SNF beds. These figures incorporate dual certified beds (i.e., beds certified for both "intermediate care facility" [ICF] and SNF) as SNF beds. It should be acknowledged here that in recent years this distinction has become redundant as a result of changes in the process of certification, including the creation of "nursing facility" beds, that resulted from the Omnibus Budget Reconciliation Act of 1987 (Coleman, 1991).

Coward, Duncan, and Uttaro (1996), using data from the 1991 *National Health Care Provider Inventory of Nursing Homes and Board and Care Homes,* have undertaken a more detailed analysis of nursing home beds by residence categories, distinguishing among three metropolitan and six nonmetropolitan residence categories. One of their most interesting findings is that occupancy levels in all nine environmental settings—from the most urban to the most rural—are remarkably similar. Occupancy levels ranged from a low of 90.6% in "counties completely rural or with an urban population fewer than 2,500, adjacent to a metro area" to a high of 92.9% in "counties in metro areas with populations between 250,000 to 999,999"; the range is only 2.3%. In attempting to provide some indication of the degree to which these figures represent comparability of demand, Coward and his colleagues conducted further analysis, revealing that two of the three metropolitan categories ("central and fringe counties of metro areas with populations of 1 million or greater," and "counties in metro areas with populations between 250,000 and 999,999") recorded a deficit of beds with respect to what would be expected as a function of the distribution of the population 65 and over, and that counties in "metro areas with populations less than 250,000" and all six nonmetropolitan categories had a surplus of beds with respect to this criterion (Coward, Duncan, & Uttaro, 1996).

NURSING HOME CARE IN RURAL AREAS

At this point it is useful to summarize what is known about rural nursing home residents and the care they receive. First, there is some evidence that residents of rural nursing homes differ from those in urban nursing homes. In 1984 Vernon Greene published a paper based on research in Arizona suggesting that:

> . . .elderly nursing home patients in rural areas tend on the average to be significantly less impaired in most areas of functional capacity, and younger at time of entry, than elderly nursing home patients in urban areas. (Greene, 1984, p. 58)

This paper led to considerable debate regarding differences between urban and rural nursing home patient populations. Recent work by Wright and Redford (1993) that analyzed minimum data set (MDS)information for Kansas also showed that residents of rural nursing homes were less functionally impaired at time of entry than were residents of urban nursing homes. The probability that the residents of rural nursing homes are less impaired than those of urban facilities is consistent with both the previously cited figures on nursing home availability (suggesting both a higher ratio of beds to population and an abundance of ICF beds) and the observation of Shaughnessy (1994, p. 151) that:

> For the most part, free standing nursing homes in rural communities tend to treat chronic care patients as opposed to patients with strong rehabilitation potential. Patients with rehabilitation potential tend to be cared for most frequently in hospital swing beds or in hospital based SNFs.

Emphasis on the provision of a higher degree of chronic care for less impaired individuals is consistent with other characteristics of rural nursing homes. For example, Shaughnessy (1994) contends that rural nursing homes tend to be philosophically pervaded by an implicit, if unstated, presumption of lengthy stays that, in turn, reinforces dependency-fostering behavior. Furthermore, consistent with this ethos, there is a propensity for less comprehensive and less frequent patient assessment than occurs in urban areas (in part, a function of the lack of available qualified staff in rural areas). One outcome, he argues, is a tendency for rural nursing homes to provide an average blend of restorative services and to focus on palliative care which tends to homogenize what may be a very diverse population and to result in less emphasis on restorative care for persons who might be able to function more independently.

This set of arguments leads to the assertion that the characteristics of contemporary rural nursing home populations reflect overprovision of facilities and overinstitutionalization of the rural elderly. As Shaughnessy (1994, p. 160) summarizes:

> In all, there is some empirical and anecdotal evidence that implies that rural elders may be overinstitutionalized in intermediate care (and possibly personal care) nursing homes. This warrants serious scrutiny from a research and evaluation perspective.

Two interrelated arguments counter this perspective. First, it can be argued that it depends upon what is meant by "overinstitutionalized." In the context of rural areas deficient in community-based long-term care, the ability to provide an alternative for persons who might be candidates for home care, were it available, may reflect a realistic response to contemporary circumstances. Rural nursing homes may already have assumed a role in providing the equivalent of assisted living housing for some of their residents who might have other options if they resided in urban areas. The second, intertwined, observation is that rural nursing homes are, almost by definition, different from urban facilities because they fulfill different needs within the long-term care system. Specifically, these points lead us to discussion of the overlap in many rural communities between the nursing home viewed as a medical facility and the nursing home considered as a residential alternative. This is a critical issue to which I return later.

Finally, it is useful to summarize what is known about the relationship between rural nursing homes and the noninstitutional care system in rural areas. Overall, this relationship, at least as reported within the literature, is poor. Several commentators have rued lack of collaboration and communication between rural nursing homes and other components of the long-term care system (Bowe, 1993; Clapp, 1993; Shaughnessy, 1994). In part, poor communication is the result of the absence in many rural areas of programs and services with which to communicate and acute shortages of professional personnel (Coward, McLaughlin, Duncan, & Bull, 1994). However, a second aspect of this separation may be the result of cultural stereotypes. Essentially, as was argued at the outset, the prevalent image of rural nursing homes (partly reinforced by our image of the role of urban nursing homes) is of an institution separated from its community context. As in the city, the rural nursing home is often stereotypically viewed through a lens of negative images, as a "world apart," an "unnatural" imposition on the rural landscape. It is conceived of as a final setting where, separated from home and community, the typical resident—reluctantly condemned by a guilt-ridden family member—awaits the grim reaper. In the following section, on the basis of a detailed case study of a single rural nursing home, I argue that this essentially urban-based image of the relationship between the nursing home and its community context is a false stereotype that, even today, may not apply to many contemporary rural nursing homes.

TOWARD A RURAL PERSPECTIVE ON RURAL NURSING HOMES: A CASE STUDY OF MOUNTAIN VIEW

As part of a project funded by the National Institute on Aging, a 3-year in-depth anthropological study was undertaken of Mountain View, a 90-bed nursing home in Stillman, a community of 2,700 located in Baden County (1990 population: 11,700) in the foothills of Appalachia (Grant number AG08475).[1] The study involved participant observation, repeated in-depth interviews (with residents, staff, family members, and other individuals living in the community), and event analyses (monitoring events in progress) (Rowles, Concotelli, & High, 1996). This methodology resulted in 1,084 transcribed interviews and more than 1,500 pages of fieldnote observations. These data facilitated description of a rural nursing home that was very much integrated within the rural community it served rather than separated from it. Blending of the nursing home with its environmental context was manifest in a variety of overlapping dimensions of *community integration.*

A level of historical integration stemmed from the origins of the nursing home. In the early 1970s a group of local residents and public officials lobbied for a facility that would allow residents needing institutional care to remain in the community rather than having to travel many miles from their home to receive nursing home care. A donation of land from a local resident at a significantly below-market reduced price and aggressive lobbying with the assistance of the governor of the state resulted in recruitment of an out-of-state corporation to construct a facility. Building the facility, largely with local labor, involved many individuals who were later to become residents. This high level of local involvement in the development of the facility resulted in a sense of ownership by the community.

Our data from Mountain View also revealed a high level of economic integration within the Stillman community. When the nursing home opened in 1975 it became one of only 22 businesses in the county to employ more than four people. Today, approximately 85% of the 79 jobs provided by the nursing home are filled by local residents who spend most of their wages in the vicinity. With an annual payroll of over $880,000 the facility provides more than 14% of the total service sector wages in the county (Division of Research and Planning, 1992). Even though the facility is corporately owned, local businesses also benefit from the presence of Mountain View, which makes over 25% of all its purchases in the community.

Perhaps the most important aspect of integration is the level of social integration revealed at Mountain View. In contrast to the prevailing image of social separation, this is a facility characterized by many kin linkages between residents and staff. As one staff member commented: "Everyone here is related to everyone else in some way." Staff members tend to develop relationships with residents, or to sustain preexisting relationships, that transcend what is found in many nursing homes. Often they will visit outside working hours. Family members often visit other residents they know in addition to their relatives. Indeed, the relaxed, almost intimate, social ambience of the nursing home is very different from the impersonal institutional aura that pervades many large urban nursing homes. Shaughnessy and his colleagues have encountered similar situations:

> . . .we have observed that staffs in a number of rural nursing homes appear to be more attentive to the functional and support needs of their residents than is typically encountered in urban nursing homes. This may be in part because rural communities are often small enough so that the nursing home staff members know and interact with the families and friends of nursing home residents in settings and circumstances apart from the nursing home. In fact it is not unusual for the nursing home staff to have known residents prior to admission to the nursing home. It may also be due to lower average turnover rates among nurses' aides in rural communities, although no national data are available to support or refute this impression. (Shaughnessy, 1994, p. 160)

Continuing social integration of Mountain View residents within the Stillman community is sustained by the high level of intergenerational obligation that is characteristic of this part of rural Appalachia (Lozier & Althouse, 1974). It is expected that families will retain a high level of involvement with relatives and friends even after they move into the nursing home. Indeed, until recently, the local newspaper would list and describe visits to the nursing home in a weekly column. This would place subtle pressure on family members to comply with the community expectation of frequent visits.

Finally, our study revealed the importance of the psychological integration of Mountain View within the Stillman community. The facility was viewed by community residents as "our nursing home." This sense of ownership has been nurtured since the opening of the facility. As Debbie Mullins, who ran the nursing home during its first year of operation, explains:

> The community was real pleased with the facility. People drifted in
> and out, you know, families, they could come any time of day or
> night to visit their mom and dad. We didn't have a senior center
> then, and older folks just came and hung out. We only had personal
> care, we had recreation, meals in the dining room, and churches
> came to give service.

This aura of openness has persisted and has become a dominant
motif of life at Mountain View: it reflects a natural and unforced
blending of the community with its long-term care facility. Such
blending is enhanced and reinforced by a high level of *institutional
permeability.*

There is constant exchange of both people and communication
between Mountain View and the Stillman community. Such permeability involves three components. First, residents frequently
make excursions out into the community. They are taken by relatives and friends to attend church, to dine at local restaurants, to
go to barbers and beauticians they have patronized for decades, to
visit relatives, to spend a day at home, or to visit the cemetery or
the old "homeplace." The staff of the facility reinforce this pattern
by taking residents on trips: to the local state park, to watch local
parades in downtown Stillman, and to participate in such activities. At the same time, Mountain View receives a constant stream
of visitors including church groups, students from the local high
school who come to interview residents for class projects, repre-
sentatives of local fast food restaurants who visit to provide cake
and punch on birthdays, and a group of local women who set up
their sewing machines in the dining room as they prepare to mend
resident's clothes. Family members visit for a special Thanksgiving
dinner or to participate in the Valentine's day celebration. Overall,
the easy flow of people and communication between Mountain
View and the Stillman community results in a blurring of the
boundary between the nursing home and its environment. Such
blurring is apparent in what appears to be lax security; visitors
come and go at all times, sometimes using the back door. When
residents leave on routine trips they sometimes forget to sign out.
While, in one sense, as a physical entity, Mountain View is a very

distinctive and visible feature of the local landscape, in another, as a community institution, it is fused with it. Thus, residents continue to identify both with a "home" and "family" outside the nursing home and at the same time with a "home" and "family" within. As Mrs. Smallwood explained one day when she came to sign out her husband: "Albert looks forward to coming home on Sundays to eat a good meal but he gets restless at about 4:00 in the afternoon and is ready to come back here."

In sum, while Mountain View remains an institutional setting where some level of autonomy is relinquished by residents, the facility reveals a plethora of characteristics that might form the basis of an enlightened philosophy of long-term care consistent with rural culture and values. In the next section I use insights from this case study in proposing such a philosophy.

ELEMENTS OF AN EXPANDED VISION

Current themes in policy debates and insights from Mountain View suggest the need for radical change both in the way we think about the rural nursing home and in the way in which this institution relates to rural society. What is required is not merely an array of new programs but rather a complete reorientation of the ethos and philosophy of care for the elderly when they become vulnerable. Several key themes must permeate this new vision.

First, rural nursing homes must be explicitly viewed as part of the community where they are located rather than separate from it. As Burton (1994, p. 794) has noted: "Nursing homes [both urban and rural] have traditionally been somewhat isolated health care facilities unrelated to other elements of the health care system." They have also tended to be isolated from the communities in which they are located—to be viewed as the somewhat foreboding place where grandma goes to die when we can no longer take care of her. The rural nursing home of the future will need to be more fully integrated, both within an expanded array of health care resources and within its community setting. Eventually the distinction between life inside the facility and life on the outside must become one of degree rather than substance with movement occurring freely between the two domains.

Second, it will be necessary to undermine the current distinction between medical and social models of care. An undermining of the medical model of nursing home care is essential (Lidz, Fischer, & Arnold, 1992). So, too, is the need for some medicalizing of contemporary nonresidential long-term care alternatives. In contrast to this need, the current trend seems to be more toward bifurcation rather than rapprochement. On the one hand, nursing home care is becoming more medicalized. Thus, in part in response to the biases of the prospective payment system, many rural nursing homes are moving toward care of a sicker short-term population—the "sicker and quicker" phenomenon. For example, in August of 1992, Mountain View became certified for skilled nursing care. With the designation of 28 of its beds for skilled care, the ambience of the facility began to undergo subtle transformation. More health professional staff were hired. The proportion of physically able and cognitively alert residents declined. In consequence, there was no longer a large enough population to merit participation in the annual wheelchair parade that had wended its way around downtown Stillman each spring during National Nursing Home Week. The frequency of other trips outside into the community began to decline. In many ways, Mountain View became less a part of the community as it became more isolated as a skilled nursing facility. On the other hand, recent policy-related literature is advocating an expanded role for the nursing home in the long-term care continuum by serving as a setting for day care, a base for home care programs, and a meeting place for civic and community organizations. This trend toward a demedicalizing of the nursing home is also apparent in links developing in some rural areas between nursing homes and housing options including assisted-living alternatives.

A third component of a new ethos pertains to the question of scale. In a very important sense, when it comes to rural nursing homes, "small is beautiful" (Shumacher, 1973). Nursing homes that are small tend to be more successful in preserving the sense of intimacy and interpersonal, rather than instrumental, relationship that is characteristic of many rural communities. Small nursing homes are able to engender the type of familylike setting that is reflective of the environments from which residents have come. It is easier for residents and staff to get to know each other and to foster a less institutional ambiance.

Fourth, and perhaps most important, there is a need for a new attitude toward residents as people—as "lives" still in process—rather than patients whose lives have ended. In this regard, recent research is documenting the degree to which, for many residents, perhaps the majority, the nature of care they receive in a nursing home is only one of many facets of their lives (Gubrium, 1993). For many, life in a nursing home is a continuation of a past rather than a separation from it. Recognizing this theme of continuity, of linkage with an experienced past, allows us to think of residents in a more humane way. Instead of "the amputee in room 22 with bed sores and a propensity to scream at night," the resident becomes "Mrs. Carole, the schoolteacher who taught several of the aides when they were in fifth grade, mother of the night nurse on the skilled unit, and former soprano in the church choir." She becomes the person who still likes to sing, enjoys French toast, and favors a seat on the front porch on summer evenings.

Rural nursing homes have tremendous potential to adapt in the directions I am advocating because of advantages inherent in rural society. As I have illustrated with respect to Mountain View, many rural nursing homes already reveal a high degree of integration within their community setting. A tendency for a high ratio of intermediate and personal care beds in relation to skilled beds serves to undermine the degree to which rural nursing homes emphasize a medical model of care. Rural nursing homes tend to be smaller and to operate on a more human scale than their urban counterparts. Rural nursing homes, because of a higher propensity for personal associations between residents and patients that often reach back over decades, possess great potential for the development of an ethos of personalization. As Shaughnessy notes, in discussing the potential for enhanced communication and coordination:

> Although we have considerable inadequacies in this regard in rural settings, the opportunity for enhanced care coordination among

providers may possibly be greater than in urban settings. This is because the sheer volume of such care is less, we have fewer providers to coordinate, and the personal rapport between patient/resident and care provider is potentially greater, as observed in the rural swing bed program. (Shaughnessy, 1994, p. 151)

Finally, in many rural areas there is an historical tradition of integrated support stemming from the time when the dominant community ethos of care for the aged involved a sense of mutual responsibility among people as part of the ongoing pattern of life. Over the generations the care that one provided for one's elders was reciprocated by one's children and by their children.

In sum, instead of remaining yet another manifestation of the way in which urban models are ineffectively and inappropriately adapted to rural conditions, there is rich potential for rural nursing homes to be in the vanguard of a new perspective on institutional long-term care that might be adapted to an urban context.

BUILDING ON INTEGRATION AND PERMEABILITY

Transforming rural nursing homes in the manner advocated above is possible if we build on recent initiatives in rural long-term care. Several trends provide grounds for optimism. One of the most visible has been the development of swing-bed programs and movement of small rural hospitals into the business of long-term care (Beaulieu, 1992; Shaughnessy, 1991, 1994; Shaughnessy, Schlenker, & Hittle, 1989; Shaughnessy, Schlenker, & Kramer, 1990; Williams, Netting, & Hood-Szivek, 1988). Swing beds allow rural hospitals to utilize excess acute care bed capacity to provide subacute or near-acute long-term care for two types of patients: (a) patients who might otherwise have to be prematurely discharged back into the community, and (b) patients who would otherwise have to travel considerable distances to obtain SNF care. This program not only provides support to rural hospitals which may make the difference between their survival and closure but also provides the equivalent of skilled nursing-home care in many rural areas lacking such facilities. Shaughnessy (1994, p. 152) suggests that "hospital swing-beds have solved the near-acute care dilemma in about 1,300 rural communities." By 1990 there were 1,289 hospitals certified for swing-bed care. This included over 50% of the 2,236 rural hospitals eligible to participate in the program in 1984. The potential of the swing-bed option was also enhanced by the passage of Omnibus Budget Reconciliation Act legislation in 1987 when the number of beds that hospitals could devote to a swing-bed program was increased from 50 to 99. Assuming continued expansion of the swing-bed option, one can envisage ever closer relationships between hospitals and nursing homes as part of an integrated long-term care continuum (Mullner, Rydman, Whiteis, & Rich, 1989). Specifically, one can anticipate an evolution of the two provider types to provide complementary roles with ". . . swing-bed hospitals serving the subacute or near-acute patient care market and community nursing homes serving the chronic care or more traditional long-term care market" (Shaughnessy, Schlenker, & Kramer, 1990, p. 67).

In addition to participation in swing-bed programs, a number of small rural hospitals have already developed long-term care units. For example, Beaulieu found that small rural hospitals with long-term care units provided about 30% of the long-term care bed capacity in the counties in which they were located (Beaulieu, 1992, p. 126).

A second aspect of innovation can be identified at the other end of the long-term care continuum. As the populations of federally supported housing projects for the elderly have aged in place, they have grown more vulnerable and more in need of supportive services (McDonald, Remus, & Laing, 1994). Such needs have ranged from various social needs for assisted-living support to significant medical support needs (Lawton, Moss, & Grimes, 1985; Sheehan & Wisensale, 1991). Unfortunately, federal housing initiatives were not designed to provide supportive services. Consequently, a major recent concern has been with providing housing managers who are not trained as caregivers with the training and resources they need to assume a caregiver role that has been thrust upon them de facto. The emergence in urban areas of a plethora of assisted living options providing varying degrees of support has been a second response to this situation (Regnier, 1994). Golant has argued that there are now many possibilities but, with respect to available options in specific locations, few choices (Golant, 1992). The lack of housing options for persons with assisted-living needs is particularly acute in rural areas. By deliberately expanding its role to involve greater provision of personal care and assisted-living options, the rural nursing home can fill a critical void in the long-term care continuum. As was pointed out earlier, there is some evidence that, historically, the rural nursing home has previously functioned in this role. Essentially, what is needed is a reconfiguration of the role of the rural nursing home in a way that would transform what historically has been implicit into an explicit component of rural long-term care policy.

Trends at the two ends of the long-term care continuum are complemented by recent advocacy for innovation in the middle—innovation and diversification in the organization and operation of nursing homes that would expand the traditional view of what such facilities provide (Noyes, 1994). It has recently been suggested that physician practices might be based in nursing homes, an option that would both provide for greater on-site physician availability for residents and, at the same time, would increase the linkage between community-based physician service and the facility (Burton, 1994). A few nursing homes already serve as the home base for home health and home care programs that extend into the community (Shaughnessy, 1994). There is a latent demand for expansion of such programs in rural areas (Kenney, 1994). Increasingly, nursing homes, including many in rural areas, are providing adult day care services (Clapp, 1993; Shaughnessy, 1994). There is a trend, not well documented as yet, toward the use of nursing home facilities for community-focused health screenings and as sites for other community-oriented services. In addition, the idea of shared facilities is gaining increased currency. For example, in his award winning anthology of innovative programs in both the United States and Europe, Regnier (1994) describes shared use of a swimming pool by a nursing home and the residents of the community in which it is located. He also cites numerous examples of long-term care facilities with restaurants that are open to the public and are well patronized by outsiders. In addition to such ad hoc innovations, initiatives blending diverse aspects of long-term care, either administratively or physically, within a campus model have a growing momentum. For example, Bowe (1993) discusses an initiative in North Dakota involving the consolidation of a rural hospital, nursing home, and physician clinics. Christensen (1982) documents the construction of adjacent "supervised living apartments" for the elderly by a rural hospital in Wisconsin. Regnier (1994) describes the close relationship between a cluster of 15 specially designed dwelling units and an adjacent nursing home in Lesja, Norway. In addition to integration of medical services and care, each of these innovations reflects ways in which nursing homes may become more permeable, more integrated into the local setting, and less isolated from their constituency.

In sum, what is needed is the development of models of rural long-term care that provide for continuity of care; allowing individuals the option to either remain in the same setting as their needs change or to move backwards and forwards among hospital, nursing home, and community residence with minimal disruption and stress as their needs change. The new rural nursing home might be the fulcrum of such a model (Bowlyow, 1990).

In presenting the argument for an expanded vision of the rural nursing home it is important to acknowledge a variety of constraints. First, the quest for integration is likely to result in a period of adjustment as systems that have for so long functioned independently, and in many respects, territorially, develop improved communication and forge new relationships. For example, there is some ambiguity with respect to the long-term care of those who are demented or for whom it is difficult to ascertain whether hospital placement or nursing home care is appropriate. At the other extreme, it is difficult to ascertain just how much assistance and, in particular, medical assistance, a potential resident should need before he or she becomes eligible for placement in a nursing home facility. In short, details of service eligibility and criteria for movement within the expanded continuum of long-term care will need to be developed; ideally, planning will occur within some type of locally monitored managed care framework.

Second, it is important to recognize the diversity of circumstances among rural areas. One model of integrated nursing-home-based rural long-term care will not fit all. Variation among rural areas is now well documented with respect to physical setting, population base, local economies, community infrastructure, service resources, and culture (Coward & Cutler, 1988; Rowles, 1988). However, until recently, there has been some reluctance to consider the pragmatic implications of such variation. One of the most important sources of diversity is variation in long-term care resources with respect to both facilities and personnel. While there is some evidence that the gap between rural and urban areas is closing (Salmon, Nelson & Rous, 1993), variations among rural areas remain considerable. Thus, some rural areas are serviced by a community hospital. Others lack this facility. Some rural areas have a wide array of community-based service programs including hospice, home care, adult day care, and transportation programs, together with a variety of special housing options for the elderly. Others are completely lacking in such resources. Consequently, it becomes essential to think in terms of approaches to long-term care that are consonant with local circumstances. The role of a local nursing home as the catalyst for change, assuming that there is a nursing home in the community, will clearly vary according to these circumstances. Rural areas with a local hospital may be able to provide subacute long-term care for their service area within this facility. In rural areas lacking a community hospital, the need to provide subacute or near-acute care may require that the local nursing home become certified to provide such care and engage in intensive efforts to recruit the skilled professional personnel (registered nurses, physical and occupational therapists) necessary to provide this level of care.

Developing the particular array of resources and programs necessary to provide a comprehensive and appropriate long-term care continuum requires sensitivity to the local social and cultural context. It is important to consider contextual intangibles including community history, local politics, the will of the community, and the idiosyncratic roles of key local leaders and nursing home owners and administrators in supporting or opposing innovation. The development of local councils or boards to examine the need for and the availability of the full range of long-term care services (from assisted-living housing to long-term skilled nursing care), as advocated by Shaughnessy (1994), may represent a useful first step in the process of exploring innovation consistent with the unique situation of each rural community.

CONCLUSIONS

Acknowledging constraints and recognizing the dangers of naive optimism, it is nonetheless appropriate to conclude with a vision of what might be. The rural nursing home of the future will be fully integrated as but one component of a long-term care continuum providing, at one extreme, either skilled nursing care within its walls or a link to subacute and near-acute long-term care in a local hospital. At the other extreme it will provide a residential option with limited assisted-living support. A blending of medical and social models of care will create a setting providing discrete support for medical needs while acknowledging the primacy of living with minimal medical intervention. Most important, the rural nursing home of the future will be integrated within its community context. It will provide a setting which fosters an easy and unrestricted flow of people, events, and ideas between the facility and the community. Ideally, the nursing home will be at the nexus of a total system of person-sensitive care that provides a seamless web of options for maximizing the quality of life of each rural resident as he or she grows progressively more frail. If we can pursue such a vision we can perhaps create the kind of nursing home (or its equivalent, for the name will surely have to change) that can, forever, expunge the negative, dread-provoking images of institutional life that all too often are today's realities.

ACKNOWLEDGMENT

The case study of Mountain View reported in this chapter was funded as part of a grant, "Family Involvement in Nursing Home

Decision Making," from the National Institute on Aging to Graham D. Rowles and Dallas M. High (AG08475). Views or opinions expressed are those of the author and do not necessarily represent the views or opinions of the funding agency.

NOTE

[1] Mountain View, Stillman, and Baden County are pseudonyms as are all identifying proper names in this chapter.

REFERENCES

Beaulieu, J. E. (1992). Small rural hospitals with long-term care: 1983-1987. *The Journal of Rural Health, 8* (2), 121–127.

Bowe, J. (1993, February). Cultivating the rural continuum of care. *Contemporary Long-Term Care*, pp. 28–30, 90.

Bowlyow, J. E. (1990). Acute and long-term care linkages: A review. *Medical Care Review, 47* (1), 75–103.

Burton, J. R. (1994). The evolution of nursing homes into comprehensive geriatrics centers: A perspective. *Journal of the American Geriatrics Society, 42,* 794–796.

Christensen, B. G. (1982, July 1). `Hospital Apartments' afford security to area's elderly. *Hospitals,* pp. 74–76.

Clapp, R. L. (1993, November/December). Health care continuum. *Nursing Homes,* pp. 7–9.

Coleman, B. (1991). *The nursing home reform act of 1987: provisions, policy, prospects.* Boston: Gerontology Institute, University of Massachusetts at Boston.

Coward, R. T., & Cutler, S. J. (1988). The concept of a continuum of residence: Comparing activities of daily living among the elderly. *Journal of Rural Studies, 4* (2), 159–168.

Coward, R. T., Duncan, R. P., & Uttaro, R. (1996). The rural nursing home industry: A national perspective. *Journal of Applied Gerontology,* 15(2), 153–171.

Coward, R. T., McLaughlin, D. K., Duncan, R. P., & Bull, C. N. (1994). An overview of health and aging in rural America. In R. T. Coward, C. N. Bull, G. Kukulka, & J. M. Galliher (Eds.) *Health services for rural elders* (pp. 1–32. New York: Springer Publishing Co.

Division of Research and Planning, (1992). *1992 Kentucky desk book of economic statistics.* Frankfort: Kentucky Cabinet for Economic Development.

Golant, S. M. (1992). *Housing America's elderly: Many possibilities/few choices.* Newbury Park, CA: Sage.

Greene, V. L. (1984). Premature institutionalization among the rural elderly in Arizona. *Public Health Reports, 99* (1), 58–63.

Gubrium, J. F. (1993). *Speaking of life: Horizons of meaning for nursing home residents.* New York: De Gruyter.

Haber, C. (1983). *Beyond sixty-five: The dilemma of old age in America's past.* Cambridge: Cambridge University Press.

Johnson, C. L., & Grant, L. A. (1985). *The nursing home in American society.* Baltimore: The Johns Hopkins University Press.

Kenney, G. M. (1993). Is access to home health care a problem in rural areas? *American Journal of Public Health. 83,* 412–414.

Lawton, M. P., Moss, M., & Grimes, M. (1985). The changing service needs of older tenants in planned housing. *The Gerontologist, 25,* 258–264.

Lidz, C. W., Fischer, L., & Arnold, R. M. (1992). *The erosion of autonomy in long-term care.* New York: Oxford University Press.

Lozier, J., & Althouse, R. (1974). Social enforcement of behavior toward elders in an Appalachian mountain settlement. *The Gerontologist, 14,* 69–80.

McDonald, M., Remus, G., & Laing, G. (1994). Research considerations: The link between housing and health in the elderly. *Journal of Gerontological Nursing. 20* (7), 5–10.

Mullner, R. M., Rydman, R. J., Whiteis, D. G., & Rich, R. F. (1989). Rural community hospitals and factors correlated with their risk of closing. *Public Health Reports. 104,* 315–325.

National Center for Health Statistics, (1992). *Prevention profile. Health, United States, 1991.* Washington, DC: U.S. Government Printing Office.

Nelson, G. (1980). Social services to the urban and rural aged: the experience of area agencies on aging. *The Gerontologist, 20,* 200–207.

Noyes, P. (1994, September). Growth in America's heartland: Bringing long-term care to where people live. *Nursing Homes,* pp. 44–45.

Pihlblad, C. T. (1975). Culture, life style, and social environment of the small town. In R. C. Atchley & T. O. Byerts (Eds.), *Rural environments and aging* (pp. 47–62). Washington, DC: Gerontological Society.

Regnier, V. (1994). *Assisted living housing for the elderly: Design innovations from the United States and Europe.* New York: Van Nostrand Reinhold.

Rowles, G. D. (1988). What's rural about rural aging? An Appalachian perspective. *Journal of Rural Studies, 4* (2), 115–124.

Rowles, G. D., Concotelli, J. A., & High, D. M. (1996). Community integration of a rural nursing home. *Journal of Applied Gerontology, 15*(2), 188–201.

Salber, E. J. (1983). *Don't send me flowers when I'm dead: Voices of rural elderly.* Durham, NC: Duke University Press.

Salmon, M. A. P., Nelson, G. M., & Rous, S. G. (1993). The continuum of care revisited: A rural perspective. *The Gerontologist, 33,* 658–666.

Shaughnessy, P. W. (1991). *Shaping policy for long-term care: Learning from the effectiveness of hospital swing beds.* Ann Arbor, MI: Health Administration Press.

Shaughnessy, P. W. (1994). Changing institutional long-term care to improve rural health care. In R. T. Coward, C. N. Bull, G. Kukulka, & G. M. Galliher (Eds.), *Health services for rural elders* (pp. 144–181). New York: Springer Publishing Co.

Shaughnessy, P. W., Schlenker, R. E., & Hittle, D. F. (1989). *Hospital swing beds: A study of long-term care provided in acute beds in rural America, 1982–1986: Vol. 1. Summary Report.* Denver: University of Colorado Health Sciences Center, Center for Health Services Research.

Shaughnessy, P. W., Schlenker, R. E., & Kramer, A. M. (1990). Quality of long-term care in nursing homes and swing-bed hospitals. *Health Services Research, 25* (1), 65–96.

Sheehan, N. W., & Wisensale, S. K. (1991). `Aging in place': Discharge policies and procedures concerning frailty among senior housing tenants. *Journal of Gerontological Social Work, 16* (1/2), 109–123.

Shumacher, E. F. (1973). *Small is beautiful: A study of economics as if people mattered.* London: Blond and Briggs.

Taietz, P., & Milton, S. (1979). Rural-urban differences in the structure of services for the elderly in upstate New York counties. *Journal of Gerontology, 34,* 429–437.

U.S. Senate, Special Committee on Aging (1974). *Nursing home care in the United States: Failure in public policy,* (Introductory Report, No. 93–1420). Washington, DC: U.S. Government Printing Office.

Williams, F. G., Netting, F. E., & Hood-Szivek, P. (1988). Developing swing-bed programs in rural Arizona hospitals. *The Gerontologist, 28,* 495–498.

Wright, L. J., & Redford, L. J. (1993 November). Analysis of functional status using the MDS+: An urban-rural comparison. Paper presented at annual national meeting of the Gerontological Society of America, New Orleans.

The Role of the Rural Hospital in Long-Term Care

7

Robert E. Schlenker
Peter W. Shaughnessy

HEALTH STATUS AND LONG-TERM CARE NEEDS OF THE RURAL ELDERLY

The elderly represent a greater percentage of the rural than of the urban population. In 1990, those age 65 and over comprised 15% of the nonmetropolitan compared to 12% of the metropolitan population (U.S. Senate, Special Committee on Aging, 1992). Data from the 1987 *National Medical Expenditure Survey (NMES)* present a similar profile utilizing three levels of urbanization and one rural category (nonmetropolitan counties with under 20,000 population). Table 7.1 presents summary population characteristics from the *NMES* (Agency for Health Care Policy and Research [AHCPR], 1994). While 14.3% of the rural population in the survey was age 65 and over, the comparable proportions for the three urban categories ranged from 9.6% to 11.6%.

As a group, the rural population does not differ significantly from the urban population in terms of the incidence of acute health problems. However, many chronic medical conditions (such as arthritis, hypertension, diabetes, and heart disease), which affect predominantly the elderly, are more prevalent in the rural population (Norton & McManus, 1989). Although this higher prevalence is associated in part with the greater proportion of elderly in rural areas, rural elderly persons also are more likely than the urban

TABLE 7.1. Selected Population Characteristics by Urban and Rural Place of Residence, United States, 1987

Population characteristic	Urban population			Rural population
	Core metropolitan	Other metropolitan	Urbanize nonmetropolitan	
Total population				
(thousands)	61,727	119,537	22,233	35,896
Percentage	25.8	49.9	9.3	15.0
Age in years (percentage distribution)				
Under 6	9.8	8.9	9.5	9.3
6–17	15.2	17.3	20.9	19.3
18–24	11.1	10.8	10.8	9.7
25–54	43.3	42.0	40.8	38.3
55–64	8.9	9.5	8.4	9.2
65 and over	11.6	11.6	9.6	14.3
Family income related to poverty status (percentage distribution)*				
Poor/near poor	18.8	14.6	22.2	25.9
Low income	13.4	12.7	18.2	16.3
Middle income	33.3	35.5	35.6	35.1
High income	34.5	37.2	24.1	22.7
Health insurance coverage (percentage distribution)				
Any private	75.6	81.5	72.9	73.9
Public only**	13.8	9.4	15.6	13.5
Uninsured all year	10.6	9.1	11.5	12.6

*Poor refers to families with incomes below the poverty line; near poor, between the poverty line and 125% of the poverty line; low income, over 125 to 200% of the poverty line; middle income, over 200% to 400% of the poverty line; and high income, over 400% of the poverty line.
**May include Medicare, Medicaid, CHAMPUS/CHAMPVA, and other state and/or local coverage.

Source: National Medical Expenditure Survey : Health Status and Access to Care of Rural and Urban Populations (Research Finding 18; AHCPR Pub. No. 9 4–0031), by the Agency for Health Care Policy and Research (AHCPR), 1994, February, Rockville, MD: U.S. Department of Health and Human Services.

elderly to have chronic health conditions that limit activity (41% versus 36% according to the 1987 *National Health Interview Survey*) (U.S. Office of Technology Assessment, 1990).

In short, the elderly, with their greater burden of functional disability and chronic illness, constitute a larger percentage of the population in rural than in urban areas (Meade, 1992). This translates into a greater need in rural areas for long-term care services for the elderly. The growing need for long-term care, which is an intensifying problem nationally, is thus actually more pronounced in rural than in urban areas.

The extent of the increasing need for long-term care in the United States (in rural and urban areas) is well documented (Mariano, 1989; Rivlin, Weiner, Hanley, & Spencer, 1988; U.S. Congress, 1990). As the population continues to age, the proportion and the number of elderly continue to increase. The resulting struggle over how best to satisfy our multiple and increasingly complex long-term care needs has been and will continue to be pronounced (U.S. Congress, 1990). Health care reform proposals typically address (and reflect) the dilemma of long-term care by both increasing long-term care coverage in order to improve access and at the same time limiting or postponing full coverage in order to contain costs.

Within the context of a growing need for long-term care by the entire population, particularly thorny problems characterize the provision of long-term care to the rural elderly, in view of the higher prevalence of chronic conditions and the challenge of providing health care in sparsely populated areas where greater travel time and distance are involved. In addition, the long-term care field has become more complex, encompassing a wide range of care needs from traditional long-term care for chronic conditions that limit cognitive and functional abilities to shorter term, medically and technologically intense rehabilitative care for postacute and subacute conditions. The growth of "short-term long-term" care has been stimulated by both advances in medical technology and Medicare's prospective payment system (PPS). Under the PPS diagnosis-related group (DRG) per-case payment for hospital care, early hospital discharge is encouraged, leading to shorter stays and greater need for postacute care (Shaughnessy & Kramer, 1990). The ability to meet the growing variety and complexity of long-term care needs is an even greater challenge in rural than in urban areas.

FINANCING, AVAILABILITY, AND USE OF LONG-TERM CARE IN RURAL AREAS

This discussion focuses on the long-term care services that are most appropriate for hospital provision—namely, the medically oriented services of nursing homes (including swing beds) and home health care. These services also are financed to a significant degree by the Medicare and Medicaid programs. Although these are the major long-term care services from the perspective of public financing, it is important to remember that the totality of long-term care includes a wide array of both formal and informal services, and includes considerably more than medical services. For example, formal social and support services include Meals-on-Wheels, companionship and household assistance, adult day care, respite care, and related services (Krout, 1994; Nelson, 1994). Informal services cover the considerable amount of care provided by spouses, other family members, and friends (Stoller & Lee, 1994). Other chapters in this book address this broad array of services in considerable depth (see Chapters 3, 4, and 5).

A major determinant of medical services availability and use is the underlying set of public financing mechanisms and eligibility requirements. Thus, the roles of Medicare and Medicaid in long-term care are summarized in this section.

Financing and Eligibility

The Medicare skilled nursing facility (SNF) benefit is exclusively a postacute skilled-level benefit covering 20 days of posthospital care with a substantial copayment for days 21–100 of covered SNF care, after which no further Medicare payment is made. Medicare home health care is also targeted at near-acute, as opposed to chronic, conditions. However, recent increases in home health length of stays and visits per admission suggest that the Medicare home health case mix may be changing to reflect a greater prevalence of chronic conditions. To be eligible for Medicare home health care, the patient must be a Medicare beneficiary and be under the care of a physician, home bound, and in need of either intermittent skilled nursing services or physical or speech therapy (Nelson, 1994). Home health services are unlimited, although the need for care must be recertified every 60 days; the patient pays no copayment or deductible. Covered home health services are skilled nursing, physical, occupational, and speech therapy; aide services, and some medical equipment and supplies.

Medicaid coverage of long-term care varies across states. When an elderly individual is eligible for Medicaid in a given state, the nursing home benefit and home care benefit cover institutional and noninstitutional chronic care services, with the extent of coverage depending on the state's Medicaid financing and coverage policies. Medicaid also covers intermediate as well as skilled-level nursing home care. Although virtually everyone is eligible for Medicare at the age of 65, Medicaid eligibility is determined largely on the basis of income and assets. Since Medicaid is the predominant public payer for nursing home care, those just above the asset and income thresholds for Medicaid eligibility (i.e., the "near poor") often constitute the most underserved. For individuals to become eligible for Medicaid, they must "spend down" to a point where their combined income and assets place them below the eligibility threshold in their state (Liu, Doty, & Manton, 1990).

As noted in Table 7.1, greater percentages of rural compared to urban populations are in the lower income groups and are without public or private insurance, which, in any case, includes little coverage of long-term care. These two factors suggest greater difficulties for rural elderly in financing long-term care through either private or public means, thus heightening the access problems faced by the rural elderly in obtaining long-term care.

In summary, Medicare pays for relatively little long-term care provided in nursing homes, but is a major payer for home health care. Medicaid, in contrast, is the dominant public payer for nursing home care, although its coverage of home care varies widely across states. Together, Medicare and Medicaid exert considerable influence over the supply and provision of both institutional and noninstitutional long-term care.

Availability

Overall, the availability of long-term care services in rural compared to urban areas is skewed toward institutional services, that is, nursing home care. Based on an analysis of Medicare's *Provider of Services* (POS) data files for 1990 (Shaughnessy, 1994), slightly over 40% (about 6,000) of all nursing homes certified for Medicare or Medicaid were in rural areas, defined as nonmetropolitan statistical areas (non-MSAs). Despite the higher average number of beds for metropolitan facilities (113 versus 83 beds), the larger number of nursing homes per capita in rural areas resulted in a considerably higher rural than urban bed-to-elderly ratio (62 versus 45 beds per 1,000 elderly). This analysis did not adjust for rural residents who receive nursing home care in metropolitan locations, but it is unlikely that such adjustments would radically change the results and, in fact, they might exacerbate this difference since anecdotal evidence suggests more rural patients travel to urban localities for nursing home care than vice versa.

Beginning in the 1980s, small rural hospitals were able to provide nursing home care in acute care beds, termed *swing beds.* Thus, measures of the availability of nursing home care in rural areas should take swing beds into account. In 1991, 1,080 rural hospitals were certified by Medicare to provide swing-bed care (Prospective Payment Assessment Commission [ProPAC], 1993). The smallest hospitals, those with fewer than 50 beds, have the highest swing-bed participation. Of the 1,009 rural hospitals with under 50 beds, 76% (764) had swing beds. Of the 669 rural hospitals in the 50- to 99-bed range, the percentage with swing beds was smaller but still included nearly half the eligible hospitals in this size range (47% or 316 hospitals). Hospitals with 100 or more beds cannot have swing beds.

The availability of home health care services cannot be precisely determined. Rural areas have considerably more home health agencies (HHAs) than urban areas (Kenney & Dubay, 1992; Redford & Severns, 1994). However, because rural agencies have only about half the staff of urban agencies, the ratio of full-time HHA staff members per 100 elderly is only slightly higher in rural areas (2.9 versus 2.6) (Hoyer, 1988). In addition, the extensive travel time and distance often involved in providing home health care in rural communities reduces the effective availability of HHA staff in rural areas. Thus, a slightly higher ratio of HHA staff members per elderly in rural areas may actually translate into a lower availability of services. In addition, other data indicate that certain home health care professionals, particularly therapists, are in short supply in rural communities. For example, a report by the Institute of Medicine (1989) indicates that per 100,000 residents of non-metropolitan compared to metropolitan communities, respectively, there were 12.7 versus 21.1 physical therapists, 14.4 versus 19.5 speech therapists, and 3.5 versus 9.3 occupational therapists. Shortages of such personnel are likely to affect most significantly those patients with rehabilitation potential who require therapy services, possibly decreasing the level of rehabilitation attained by many rural elderly and increasing the tendency toward nursing home institutionalization.

Use

The use of long-term care services generally follows the supply (availability) patterns just presented. The rural elderly, per person, use more nursing home care (including swing-bed care) and less home health care than the urban elderly. Although Medicare data relate to only a portion of long-term care use, particularly for nursing home care, the patterns are informative. Using 1987 data, Dubay (1993) found that rural Medicare enrollees use the Medicare SNF benefit at a rate that is 15% higher than the rate for urban enrollees. Her data include SNF care provided via swing beds, and indicate that almost 29% of SNF admissions in rural areas are to swing beds. Dubay concludes that the swing-bed program is critical in providing access to postacute SNF care for the rural elderly.

Swing-bed care is most frequently short-term long-term care, and swing beds are typically used as "holding beds" until long-term care patients are sufficiently rehabilitated to return home (at times, with home health care) or until a nursing home bed becomes available in the community. The average length of stay for all swing-bed patients in the mid-1980s was approximately 20 days, while the average stay for Medicare swing-bed patients was about 14 days (Shaughnessy, 1991).

Data on non-SNF nursing home care (i.e., care provided by intermediate care facilities [ICFs]), are not readily available. However, rough estimates made by Shaughnessy (1994) suggest that ICF use rates are considerably higher in rural compared to urban areas. Together, the SNF, ICF, and swing-bed data indicate higher overall nursing home use by rural compared to urban elders.

With regard to home health care, Medicare data are likely to cover the majority of such services received by the elderly. A recent analysis of 1983, 1985, and 1987 data (Kenney, 1993) suggests lower home health use rates in rural relative to urban areas (44.5 versus 50.6 users per 1,000 Medicare enrollees in 1987), although once they receive care, rural home health patients obtain on average three more visits than their urban counterparts (25.8 versus 22.6 visits). However, the rural population was much less likely to receive therapy or medical social service visits, a finding that is consistent with the lower availability, mentioned above, of personnel to provide such services.

Further evidence, focused on two conditions, is provided by a study of Medicare patients with diabetes or who had undergone surgical hip procedures (Cheh & Phillips, 1993). The results suggest that rural patients with these conditions receive fewer visits than urban patients with the same conditions. Specifically, a lower percentage of rural patients with these conditions received the guideline number of visits specified for the study by a panel of home health experts. The difference was particularly striking for physical therapy visits. Although the evidence suggested that to some extent skilled nursing services substitute for physical therapy services in rural areas, the combined total of skilled nursing and physical therapy services still fell below the guideline number of visits proportionately more for rural than for urban patients.

Thus, although the available research on long-term care use by the elderly is not comprehensive, the findings suggest a pattern of greater institutionalization for long-term care in rural compared to urban areas, and lower use of home health services, particularly rehabilitation-oriented therapy services.

THE RURAL HOSPITAL IN LONG-TERM CARE

The rural hospital's role in long-term care must be considered in the context of its community role. The rural hospital, more so than its urban counterpart, is typically an integral and major component of the community. It is a source of community identity and pride as well as a major employer and purchaser in the local economy (Duncan, 1994; Ermann, 1990). The difficulties faced by rural hospitals over the past decade therefore have had community-wide effects. According to a report by the Prospective Payment Assessment Commission (ProPAC, 1994), between 1980 and 1992 the number of rural hospitals declined by nearly 21% (from 3,174 to 2,590). The major reason for the hospital closures was decreasing demand for inpatient services due in large part to the implementation of Medicare's PPS for hospital care (Ermann, 1990). Among the hospitals that have survived, a common response to the pressures induced by PPS has been increased diversification into long-term care and other services.

Rural hospitals are presently more involved than urban hospitals in long-term care provision, and this pattern of greater involvement has been increasing over time. Table 7.2 provides data on the percentage of hospitals in rural compared to urban areas providing home health and skilled nursing services for 1985, 1990, and 1992 (ProPAC, 1994). (The data on skilled nursing services for 1990 and 1992 in the table exclude swing beds.) The proportions of rural compared to urban hospitals providing home health and skilled nursing care are greater and the gap appears to have widened over time. The significant role of rural hospitals in long-term care also is identified by Beaulieu (1992), who found that hospitals with long-term care units contributed nearly 30% of the total long-term care bed supply in their counties. Consistent with the hypothesis that long-term care provision often results from declining acute care financial viability, Beaulieu further found that hospitals that were more likely to have long-term care units during

Table 7.2. Percentage of Home Health and Skilled Nursing Services Provided by Community Hospitals, by Location, Selected Years

Location/year	Home health	Skilled nursing*
All Hospitals		
1985	29.7%	18.8%
1990	35.6	22.3
1992	38.0	34.0
Urban		
1985	31.8	11.1
1990	34.4	18.7
1992	35.8	26.0
Rural		
1985	27.4	27.6
1990	37.1	26.4
1992	40.9	44.4

*Data for 1985 reflect the presence of skilled nursing services anywhere in the hospital. Data for 1990 and 1992 reflect the presence of a separate skilled nursing unit (i.e., excluding swing beds).

Source: Report and Recommendations to the Congress, by Prospective Payment Assessment Commission (ProPAC), March 1, 1994, in *Medicare and Medicaid Guide,* 792 (Part 2). Chicago, IL: Commerce Clearing House.

1983–1987 also had lower occupancy rates and higher expenses per acute admission both before and after developing their long-term care unit.

Although a greater proportion of rural than urban hospitals provided skilled nursing care in all three years shown in Table 7.2, greater rural hospital involvement in home health care appears to be a more recent phenomenon. In 1985, the proportion of hospitals providing home health care was lower in rural than in urban areas (27.4% versus 31.8%), but the turnaround by 1992 was dramatic (to 40.9% versus 35.8%). The importance of rural hospitals in home health care provision also is demonstrated by Hoyer's (1988) finding that 32% of rural home health agencies were hospital based, compared to 20% of urban agencies.

The increasing involvement of rural hospitals in long-term care provision is in part a response to financial pressures, as noted above, but the trend also represents a response to community needs by rural hospitals in their role as the focal point of health care in their communities. Rural hospitals have diversified into long-term care not only for financial reasons, but also to address a perceived strong community need for such services. In fact, financial considerations often are not extensively involved in the decision process (Shaughnessy, 1991), which can lead to difficulties for hospitals, as discussed further below.

The swing-bed program allowed many hospitals to enter the long-term care field more easily than would otherwise have been possible. This resulted from the less rigid Medicare requirements for swing-bed participation relative to the establishment of a distinct-part SNF unit. Consequently, experience with the swing-bed program enabled many hospital staff, including both administrative and patient care personnel, to become familiar with the provision of subacute long-term care. This, in turn, encouraged hospitals to expand into additional long-term care areas, by developing a distinct-part SNF unit, a home health care program, or a hospice program (Shaughnessy, 1991).

THE IMPORTANCE OF CARE PLANNING AND COORDINATION

Although the swing-bed program demonstrated many positive aspects of hospital involvement in long-term care, it also revealed some shortcomings that highlight the need for a coordinated approach to long-term care in rural communities. For example, our evaluation of swing-bed hospitals nationally (Shaughnessy et al., 1989) found that postacute care patients received higher quality subacute care in swing-bed hospitals relative to rural nursing homes, with quality measured in terms of improvement in functional and physiologic outcomes. In fact, the study showed that swing-bed patients were able to return home sooner and with greater frequency than comparable rural nursing home patients. At the same time, the quality of chronic care often was better in rural nursing homes than in swing-bed hospitals, particularly for services related to functional disabilities and incontinence. Rural hospitals were less well able to provide traditional institutional long-term care to patients with chronic care needs than were rural nursing homes, largely due to the differences in training and orientation of the nursing and aide staffs in the two settings. That is, even in the swing-bed units of rural hospitals, the nursing staff was oriented toward treatment of acute care conditions, and less aware of and responsive to the patients' chronic care needs.

The swing-bed example thus highlights the critical importance of integrated care planning and coordination in rural long-term care. This applies to transitions from acute to postacute care and to the provision of chronic care services (particularly to determine the appropriate combination of institutional and noninstitutional services). Hospitals involved in long-term care can take a lead role in such integration, building on the in-hospital systems already in place. In swing-bed environments, for example, such coordination is facilitated because the patient remains in the same institution, often with the same nursing staff. The physician also continues to be involved on a more regular basis than if the patient is transferred to a nursing home, particularly a nursing home that is not affiliated with the hospital or is located in another community. Such coordination can be readily expanded if the hospital also provides traditional nursing-homelike care in a special unit and administers home health care as well. Even if such long-term care services are provided by other organizations, rural hospitals can take the lead in expanding care coordination mechanisms and approaches.

Care coordination should ensure that multidisciplinary care planning, appropriate interventions, and timely reassessment and monitoring of patient/resident condition all occur. This requires communication among acute and long-term care providers, including nursing homes, home health programs, assisted living settings, outpatient or day care programs, and swing-bed hospitals. Despite the difficulties resulting from provider scarcity, rural areas have some advantages in terms of their potential for expanded coordination. Fewer patients and providers are involved, and personal relationships among providers and between providers and patients may be greater than in urban areas (Shaughnessy, 1991). If the hospital takes the lead coordinating role, and in particular if the hospital also provides many of the needed services, coordination is likely to be facilitated. As part of the integrative role, hospital involvement in long-term care can also lead to an increased emphasis on rehabilitation services. In view of the emerging greater recognition of the rehabilitation potential of many elderly patients, the acute care base of the hospital, suggesting to staff and patients that stays will be short and that discharge is expected, can contribute to the successful provision of rehabilitative services to the elderly.

FUTURE PROSPECTS FOR RURAL HOSPITALS IN LONG-TERM CARE

The rural hospital sector is undergoing a significant transformation with an uncertain outcome. Many rural hospitals have closed. Those that have survived have pursued several strategies (Moscovice, 1989; Moscovice, Johnson, Finch, Grogan, & Krawlewski, 1991). Some hospitals have reduced their services to provide mainly primary care, emergency services, and limited acute inpatient services. Others have diversified and expanded into other services, including long-term care. Still others have pursued network and consortium arrangements involving both vertical and horizontal integration efforts, such arrangements can include long-term care. Contract management is another survival strategy, used by a greater proportion of rural than urban hospitals—19% versus 8% in 1987 (Dor, 1994); such management approaches may also include long-term care. Thus, long-term care provision is often pursued by rural hospitals as a means of hospital diversification, which not only provides a needed service but also may help rural hospitals to survive financially.

Several factors, both positive and negative, face hospitals that wish to move into long-term care. The following factors, discussed in the remainder of this section, are major forces that will shape the future role of rural hospitals in long-term care: (a) programs to assist rural hospitals; (b) the risks facing hospitals diversifying into long-term care; (c) changes in care practices and technology; (d) hospital and community characteristics; (e) public policy issues; and (f) research.

Programs to Assist Rural Hospitals

Various federal programs have been developed to assist rural hospitals. For example, a rural hospital's Medicare reimbursement can be increased if it is designated a "sole community" hospital, a Medicare-dependent small rural hospital, or a "disproportionate share" hospital. Two other public and private programs that have been developed to assist hospitals with diversification into areas such as long-term care are the Essential Access Community Hospital (EACH) program (Campion, 1993) and the Robert Wood Johnson Foundation (RWJF) Hospital-Based Rural Health Care Program (Moscovice et al., 1991; Weisfeld, 1993).

The EACH program is a joint federal-state effort to assure the availability of primary care, emergency services, and limited acute inpatient services in rural areas where it is no longer feasible to maintain full-service hospitals. Under the program, rural primary care hospitals (PCHs) establish a network relationship with a larger supporting EACH facility. With respect to long-term care, PCHs can provide skilled nursing services in a distinct SNF and/or in a swing-bed program and also can provide home health services. The program currently involves seven states: California, Colorado, Kansas, New York, North Carolina, South Dakota, and West Virginia.

The RWJF Hospital-Based Rural Health Care Program also facilitates rural hospital diversification into nursing home and home health care. This program is similar in concept to another RWJF program which assists state hospital associations and rural hospitals to develop swing-bed programs (Shaughnessy, 1991). Although these and other programs are not universally available to hospitals, their existence demonstrates the recognition by public and private funders of the rural hospital's changing role and its potential in the long-term care area.

Long-Term Care Diversification Risks

Significant risks also face rural hospitals diversifying into long-term care. The hospital must be committed to the provision of long-term care and recognize the major differences in care needs between acute- and long-term care patients, even for short-term long-term care patients. A long-term care orientation must be accepted by the patient care staff and physicians. As evidenced by the experience of the swing-bed program, this expansion in orientation often requires time, training/education, and continuing reinforcement. Although the experience of the swing-bed program is somewhat unique in that acute care staff also provide the long-term care services to swing-bed patients, a recognition of the different orientation required for long-term care patients is vital to any form of hospital diversification into long-term care.

Financial planning also is critical and sometimes not adequately addressed by rural hospitals intent on meeting the care needs of their communities. Reimbursement is essential to financial viability under any diversification strategy. Hospitals planning to diversify into long-term care thus must be cognizant of the probable payer mix of their long-term care patients (i.e., the proportion of care that would be covered through private insurance, Medicare, Medicaid, self-pay, or other sources) and must be completely familiar with Medicare and Medicaid reimbursement policies for hospital-based SNF, ICF, swing-beds, and home health care. For example, Medicare reimbursement for ancillary services provided to swing-bed patients is based on the methodology that pertained to all hospital ancillary services before PPS. Thus, if a patient is transferred from acute to swing-bed status, Medicare will reimburse for that patient's ancillary services, whereas if the patient remained in acute care, the PPS DRG payment would be assumed to cover such ancillary services (Schlenker & Shaughnessy, 1989).

Changes in Long-Term Care Practices and Technology

Rural hospitals involved in long-term care must monitor and, if possible, anticipate changes in our rapidly evolving health care system. For instance, innovative programs in rehabilitative care and therapy services for the elderly are likely to yield new opportunities for rural hospitals, either to provide such services directly or to establish access to them for their elderly patients through various integrated programs involving other providers (Kramer et al., 1991). Further, the ability to recruit therapy personnel is likely to be enhanced for hospitals with such programs.

As another example, advances in *telemedicine* (i.e., the application of telecommunications technology for the delivery of health care across long distances) may provide the potential for greater access to physician specialty consultation and related services (Grigsby, Kaehny, Schlenker, Shaughnessy, & Beale, 1993; Grigsby et al., 1994). In the long-term care area, various monitoring and communication technologies are likely to develop that will reduce the number of visits and total travel time required to provide home health care in sparsely populated areas. Rural hospitals may be appropriate sites for such technologically advanced home health care approaches.

The Importance of Hospital and Community Characteristics

Hospital and community characteristics influence both the opportunities and the constraints facing rural hospitals wishing to move into long-term care. Smaller hospitals usually lack extensive resources to carry out diversification strategies. A viable alternative may be to act through consortia of rural hospitals or of urban and rural hospitals. Although larger rural hospitals are likely to have more resources available to plan and implement new programs, they also may face different constraints. For example, rural hospitals with 100 or more beds cannot participate in the swing-bed program, and those with 50–99 beds must transfer Medicare patients requiring skilled-level nursing care to a Medicare SNF within 5 days unless a physician certifies this is not appropriate (Shaughnessy, 1994). Similarly, community characteristics such as population demographics, payer mix, and the supply of health professionals significantly influence opportunities and constraints. Individual hospitals must take such diverse factors into account when considering long-term care provision. From a policy and research perspective, it is important to try to predict the effects of hospital and community characteristics on hospital performance in long-term care.

Public Policy Issues

Many federal and state policies affect the opportunities and risks facing rural hospitals in long-term care. Medicare and Medicaid reimbursement policies often create perverse financial incentives for rural hospitals. For instance, as noted earlier, hospitals have incentives to transfer patients to swing-bed from acute care to obtain higher Medicare reimbursement for ancillary services. If such a transfer is premature, a subsequent acute care episode may result, which adversely affects the patient and also increases over-all Medicare expenditures. As another example, Medicare reimbursement for SNF routine care usually is higher for distinct SNFs than for swing-bed care. This may encourage inappropriate SNF placement when swing-bed placement would be optimal. Similarly, reimbursement differences and cost structures between hospital-based home health care and nursing home care may influence the decision to encourage patient placement either at home or in the nursing home. These issues highlight the importance of developing an integrated rural long-term care payment policy.

Another important policy issue related to long-term care is physician reimbursement. Under Medicare and Medicaid, for example, physicians are more readily reimbursed for visits to patients in hospitals than in nursing homes. Thus, there have been strong disincentives for physician involvement in long-term care in general and home health care in particular. Physician reimbursement for home health care plan oversight was implemented as of January 1,1995, however, which may increase physician involvement in home health care. These and related rural health policy issues deserve careful analysis, as exemplified by the work of Kiel (1993), Christianson and Moscovice (1993), and Coburn et al. (1994).

Need for Research

As rural long-term care issues and the role of rural hospitals in addressing those issues continue to evolve, ongoing health services research is needed to both learn from and inform the process. For example, the practice pattern and technological trends noted above require careful assessment and evaluation. The role of hospital size and community characteristics in long-term care community needs and hospital involvement in addressing those needs also must be better understood. Also, the potential impacts of any federal or state health care reform proposals on rural health care in general and on the role of hospitals in providing health care to elderly residents of rural areas in particular require careful policy analysis and research.

CONCLUSIONS AND RECOMMENDATIONS

Key requirements for the successful provision of long-term care to the elderly, particularly the rural elderly, are that it be well integrated and focused on patient needs. It also must include the transfer of information from one provider setting to another and the proper monitoring and follow-up of the patient. The need for integrated care also extends beyond medical care and encompasses the social and support services required by the patient/client.

Although the appropriate role for the rural hospital in coordinating and providing long-term care depends on community circumstances such as provider availability and interrelationships, the role often can be a major one. The hospital is in a unique position to provide, coordinate, and integrate long-term care and acute care in rural communities. In such a role, the hospital can meet a growing community need in rural areas and can thereby adjust to the lessened demand for acute care services in the present and future health care environment. Increased long-term care involvement by rural hospitals can be undertaken by individual hospitals as well as by groups of hospitals under consortia and network arrangements. All such approaches, however, require careful planning, particularly with respect to organization, staffing, and financing. In addition, collaborative coordination is essential between health care service providers and organizations providing the many other services required by the rural elderly, in particular social and support services. Hospitals can play a key role in fostering such coordination.

The following recommendations are intended to facilitate rural hospital involvement in long-term care. The recommendations emphasize reimbursement policy actions because of the critical financial situation of many rural hospitals. Other actions to promote hospital involvement in long-term care are, of course, important, but reimbursement increases appear to be essential.

Aggressive public relations. Organizations and associations whose mission entails promoting and enhancing health and health care for rural communities should embark on an information dissemination campaign regarding the gaps in our long-term care delivery system in rural America. The considerable value of the role rural hospitals can play in providing and coordinating long-term care in rural areas should be clearly and convincingly articulated as one of the main themes of this campaign. The nature of such a role played by rural hospitals is radically different and has far greater potential to serve the community than an analogous role that might be played by urban hospitals.

Comprehensive evaluations. Public and private programs that have encouraged rural hospital diversification into long-term care through grant support, information dissemination, technical assistance, continuing education, and related approaches should be comprehensively evaluated as a group as well as individually.

The objectives of an overall evaluation would be to identify the comparative strengths and weaknesses of the various programs, and, in particular, to identify hospital characteristics, community factors, and specific program and hospital strategies that facilitate or impede the success of hospital long-term care provision. The results of such an evaluation could serve as the basis for expanded programs of this type.

Gradual change. For hospitals with relatively little experience in long-term care, it is important to proceed in a staged manner, so that limited administrative, financial, and organizational resources are not overextended. The swing-bed program represents one way that a hospital can move into long-term care in phases, without the substantial changes that are required when establishing a distinct nursing home unit. In addition, the potential of swing-bed care could be increased by eliminating federal regulations that currently constrain swing-bed hospitals with 51–99 beds, such as the required transfer of patients to distinct SNF units within 5 days.

Enhanced public funding. Medicare and Medicaid reimbursement to rural hospitals involved in long-term care should be increased. Although grant programs can facilitate start-up activities for hospitals diversifying into long-term care, ongoing financing is needed. For example, to encourage rural hospital diversification into integrated long-term care service provision, additional reimbursement could be tied to the number of long-term care services provided. As an illustration, considering swing-bed, SNF, and home health care as three distinct long-term care service programs, total reimbursement from Medicare (or Medicaid) for all such long-term care services provided by the hospital could be increased by 2% if one such program were provided, by 6% if two such programs were provided, and by 10% if all three programs were provided. To qualify for additional reimbursement, the hospital would be required to demonstrate evidence of a strong and effective care integration program. This could be assessed as part of the Medicare/Medicaid certification process.

Support for physician involvement. Although higher reimbursement increases Medicare and Medicaid outlays, it will be cost-effective if it prevents or reduces hospital admissions or admissions to long-term care facilities in higher cost urban areas. To strengthen the integrative aspect of this approach, physician reimbursement for rural long-term care provided through hospital programs also should be increased. In particular, reimbursement should be provided to physicians for a greater number of visits to long-term care patients in rural facilities and for home health case management in rural areas.

Monitor changes. Reimbursement changes should be implemented on a demonstration basis initially, and subjected to careful evaluation.

The preceding suggestions are illustrative, and other approaches also deserve consideration. In all cases, evaluation of new efforts and their effects is critical. Nevertheless, our contention is that programs and policies to initiate and maintain greater rural hospital involvement in long-term care, such as those suggested here, bear significant promise to improve long-term care for rural elders.

REFERENCES

Beaulieu, J. E. (1992). Small rural hospitals with long-term care: 1983 to 1987. *The Journal of Rural Health, 8,* 121–127.

Campion, D. M. (1993). *A report from the Technical Resource Center on alternative rural hospital models.* Washington, DC: Alpha Center.

Cheh, V., & Phillips, B. (1993). Adequate access to posthospital home health services: Differences between urban and rural areas. *The Journal of Rural Health, 9,* 262–269.

Christianson, J., & Moscovice, I. (1993, Fall). Health care reform and rural health networks. *Health Affairs,* pp. 59–75.

Coburn, A. F., Cordes, S. M., Crittenden, R. A., Hart, J. P., Mueller, K. J., Myers, W. W., & Ricketts, T. R. (1994). An expert panel approach to assessing the rural implications of health care reform: The case of the Health Security Act. *The Journal of Rural Health, 10,* 6–15.

Dor, A., (1994, April). *Are contract-managed hospitals more efficient?* (Agency for Health Care Policy and Research, Provider Studies Research Note 21. AHCPR Pub. No. 94–0004). Rockville, MD: U.S. Department of Health and Human Services.

Dubay, L. C. (1993). Comparison of rural and urban skilled nursing facility benefit use. *Health Care Financing Review, 14* (4), 25–37.

Duncan, R. P. (1994). Rural hospitals and rural elders. In R. T. Coward, C. N. Bull, G. Kukulka, & J. M. Galliher (Eds.), *Health services for rural elders.* New York: Springer Publishing Co.

Ermann, D. A. (1990). Rural health care: The future of the hospital. *Medical Care Review, 47*(1), 33–73.

Grigsby, J., Kaehny, M. M., Schlenker, R. E., Shaughnessy, P. W., & Beale, S. K. (1993). *Telemedicine: Literature review and analytic framework.* (DHHS Contract No. 500–92–0046). Denver, CO: Center for Health Policy Research.

Grigsby, J., Sandberg, E. J., Kaehny, M. M., Kramer, A. M., Schlenker, R. E., & Shaughnessy, P. W. (1994). *Case studies and current status of telemedicine.* (DHHS Contract No. 500–92–0046). Denver, CO: Center for Health Policy Research.

Hoyer, R. G. (1988, September). Urban and rural home health agencies: Some geographic differences. *Caring,* pp. 50–53.

Institute of Medicine (IOM) (1989). *Allied health services: Avoiding crises.* Washington, DC: National Academy.

Kenney, G. M. (1993). Rural and urban differentials in Medicare home health use. *Health Care Financing Review, 14* (4), 39–57.

Kenney, G. M., & Dubay, L. D. (1992). Examining area variation in the use of Medicare home health services. *Medical Care, 30* (1), 43–57.

Kiel, J. M. (1993). How state policy affects rural hospital consortia: The rural health care delivery system. *The Milbank Quarterly, 71,* 625–643.

Kramer, A. M., Schlenker, R. E., Shaughnessy, P. W., Tropea, D. A., Hrincevich, C. A., & Ahmad, L. A. (1991). *Evaluation of innovative rehabilitation alternatives and critical dimensions of rehabilitation care: Concept paper.* Center for Health Services Research, University of Colorado Health Sciences Center.

Krout, J. A. (1994). Rural aging community-based services. In R. T.

Coward, C. N. Bull, G. Kukulka, & J. M. Galliher (Eds.), *Health services for rural elders.* New York: Springer Publishing Co.

Liu, K., Doty, P., & Manton, K. (1990). Medicaid spenddown in nursing homes. *The Gerontologist, 30,* 7–15.

Mariano, L. (1989). Growth of the Medicare population. *Health Care Financing Review, 10* (3), 123–124.

Meade, M. S. (1992). Implications of changing demographic structures for rural health services. In W. M. Gesler & T. C. Ricketts (Eds.), *Health in rural North America* (pp. 69–85). New Brunswick, NJ: Rutgers University Press.

Moscovice, I. (1989). Strategies for promoting a viable rural health care system. *The Journal of Rural Health, 5,* 216–230.

Moscovice, I., Johnson, J., Finch, F., Grogan, C., & Kralewski, J. (1991). The structure and characteristics of rural hospital consortia. *The Journal of Rural Health, 7,* 575–588.

Nelson, G. M. (1994). In-home services for rural elders. In R. T. Coward, C. N. Bull, G. Kukulka, & J. M. Galliher (Eds.), *Health services for rural elders.* New York: Springer Publishing Co.

Norton, C. H., & McManus, M. A. (1989). Background tables on demographic characteristics, health status, and health services utilization. *Health Services Research, 23,* 725–756.

Prospective Payment Assessment Commission (ProPAC) (1993). Medicare and the American health care system. Report to Congress, June 1993. *Medicare and Medicaid Guide, 751* (Part 2). Chicago, IL: Commerce Clearing House.

Prospective Payment Assessment Commission (ProPAC) (1994). Report and recommendations to the Congress, March 1, 1994. *Medicare and Medicaid Guide, 792* (Part 2). Chicago, IL: Commerce Clearing House.

Redford, L. J., & Severns, A. B. (1994). Home health services in rural America. In J. A. Krout (Ed.), *Providing community-based services to the rural elderly.* Thousand Oaks, CA: Sage.

Rivlin, A., Weiner, J., Hanley, R., & Spence, D. (1988). *Caring for the disabled elderly: Who will pay?* Washington, DC: Brookings Institution.

Schlenker, R. E., & Shaughnessy, P. W. (1989). Swing-bed hospital cost and reimbursement. *Inquiry, 26,* 508–521.

Shaughnessy, P. (1991). *Shaping policy for long term care: Learning from the effectiveness of hospital swing beds.* Ann Arbor, MI: Health Administration Press.

Shaughnessy, P. (1994). Changing institutional long-term care to improve rural health care. In R. T. Coward, C. N. Bull, G. Kukulka, & J. M. Galliher (Eds.), *Health services for rural elders.* New York: Springer Publishing Co.

Shaughnessy, P. W., & Kramer, A. M. (1990). The increased needs of patients in nursing homes and patients receiving home health care. *New England Journal of Medicine 322,* 21–27.

Shaughnessy, P., Schlenker, R., & Hittle, D., Harden, S., Spencer, M., Beck, D., Vahling, D., Grant, W., Mason, L., McGloin, J., Amirani, J., McFarlane II, A., Graff, S., DeVore, P., & Van Epps, W. (1989). *Hospital swing beds: A study of long-term care provided in acute care beds in rural America, 1982–1986, Volume I: Summary report.* Denver, CO: Center for Health Services Research, University of Colorado Health Sciences Center.

Stoller, E. P., & Lee, G. R. (1994). Informal care of rural elders. In R. T. Coward, C. N. Bull, G. Kukulka, & J. M. Galliher (Eds.), *Health services for rural elders.* New York: Springer Publishing Co.

U.S. Senate, Special Committee on Aging (1992). *Common beliefs about the rural elderly: Myth or fact?* Washington, DC: U.S. Government Printing Office.

U.S. Office of Technology Assessment (OTA). (1990). *Health care in rural America.* (OTA Publication No. OTA-H-434). Washington, DC: U.S. Government Printing Office.

U.S. Congress, The Pepper Commission: U.S. Bipartisan Commission on Comprehensive Health Care. (1990). *A call for action.* (Final Report, S. Prt. 101–114.) Washington, DC: U.S. Government Printing Office.

Weisfeld, V. D. (Ed.). (1993). *Rural health challenges in the 1990s: Strategies from the hospital-based rural health care program.* Princeton, NJ: The Robert Wood Johnson Foundation.

Health Reform and Rural Long-Term Care

8

Andrew F. Coburn

The goals of long-term care reform are well known. They are:

1. Expand the range of noninstitutional services available to the elderly and the disabled to enable them to live more independently in their own homes or in homelike environments.

2. Develop an equitable method for financing long-term care services with an appropriate balance of public and private resources.

3. Expand support for family members and other informal caregivers.

4. Improve the education, training, and salaries for attracting personnel and improving quality in the long-term care system (Kane & Kane, 1987; Rivlin, Wiener, Hanley, & Spence, 1988; Wiener & Illston, 1994).

Achievement of these goals has been elusive, however, and their attainment in rural areas is even more problematic. As all of the chapters in this volume have noted, rural communities and populations face a number of very difficult problems in developing appropriate and effective long-term care systems, including demographics characterized by low incomes and high dependency ratios, limited availability of many of the services that constitute essential elements of the long-term care continuum, and the limited availability of trained health professionals and paraprofessionals (Beaulieu, 1994). However, as Schlenker and Shaughnessy (Chapter 7) note in their discussion of the role of rural hospitals in long-term care, there are also rural assets and opportunities for building long-term care in rural areas.

This chapter discusses the implications of national health care reform for rural long-term care. My goal is to name and discuss some of the key, and enduring, policy issues raised in the recent health reform debate that may have important implications for rural long-term care. There are three parts to this discussion. First, there are the provisions specific to long-term care proposed in national reform bills that merit scrutiny for their impact on rural life. Debate over these provisions rarely, if ever, focused on their implications for rural people and places. For the most part, concern over these long-term care provisions has focused on whether and how the expansion of long-term care benefits could be financed.

A second important dimension of health care reform has to do with provisions in the health reform legislation debated in the 103rd Congress. Proposed changes in primary and acute care systems would undoubtedly affect rural long-term care systems.

And finally, independent of reform, it is important to consider the implications for rural long-term care of the rapid, market-driven changes in the reconfiguration of health care providers—urban and rural—into networks and managed care systems. Health care providers are not waiting for national reform to transform themselves into new organizational and financial structures that can survive in an increasingly competitive health care marketplace. These changes are likely to have far-reaching implications, both positive and negative, for rural long-term care.

NATIONAL REFORM LEGISLATION

Long-Term Care Provisions

Despite variation in the specific long-term care provisions of specific health reform legislation considered by the 103rd Congress, the fundamental goals of long-term care reform have been similar across bills:

1. Redress the imbalance in institutional versus home care services by expanding entitlements to a broader array of in-home and community services.

2. Expand private investments in long-term care insurance as a means for reducing the burden on public programs, notably Medicare and Medicaid.

3. Contain rising long-term care costs, particularly for Medicaid and Medicare.

4. Promote greater integration of the primary and acute care system with long-term care.

Each of these goals, and more specifically, the policy strategies proposed to address them, deserve discussion regarding their implications for improving the availability, accessibility and quality of long-term care in rural areas.

Expanding home care and community services
The institutional bias in the organization and financing of long-term care has been widely discussed for the past decade (Kane & Kane, 1987; Rivlin et al., 1988). Work by Shaughnessy (1994) showing higher ratios of nursing home beds to population and higher use rates among populations in rural areas suggests that this bias is even more evident there than in metropolitan areas. As Krout (Chapter 5) and Magilvy (Chapter 4) note, the enduring problems of distance and transportation barriers, limited provider and service availability (particularly rehabilitation and social services), and program eligibility criteria, have conspired to make home- and community-based services less available and accessible in

rural than urban areas.

Recognizing the imbalance between institutional and noninstitutional services in the current long-term care system, policymakers have sought to expand public and private financing of home- and community-based services, including personal care, homemaker, adult day care and home health services. Health reform legislation considered by the 103rd Congress, including President Clinton's Health Security Act (H.R. 3600) and Senator Mitchell's so-called compromise (S. 2357), contained provisions creating a new, limited and capped, entitlement program for home- and community-based services to be administered by the states. Although these provisions would have provided a broader base of financing for home care services, they were not sufficient to ensure the availability or accessibility of such services in rural, underserved communities and populations.

Two related problems are especially important in this regard. First, there is no assurance that benefits provided to individuals will produce more accessible and affordable services in traditionally underserved rural areas. For example, entitlements or insurance benefits alone will not overcome the problem in some rural areas of recruiting and training paraprofessionals, such as personal care attendants (PCAs), to provide in-home services. Patterns of service use generally correspond to the supply characteristics in rural areas (Schlenker & Shaughnessy, Chapter 7). The lack of infrastructure for the development and delivery of in-home services in many areas, however, represents a significant impediment to making expanded home care benefits and services more available and accessible in rural communities. Although rural hospitals and senior centers could serve as key building blocks in the development of such an infrastructure, there are numerous barriers and problems to overccome. For example, the development of appropriate financing and reimbursement systems must occur before rural communities can capitalize more fully on the potential of these organizational entities.

Although expanding home care services is vital to redressing the current institutional bias in the long-term care system, additional services and facilities, such as residential care, are also needed to achieve this goal. Unfortunately, we know very little about the availability of residential, long-term care options in rural areas. What we do know is that despite higher rates of home ownership among rural elderly, alternative housing options are more likely to be limited in most rural areas (Beaulieu, 1994).

The development and expansion of residential long-term care options was beyond the scope of the national health reform debate. There was little if anything in health care reform legislation that would have significantly enhanced residential options for the disabled elderly. The states continue to lead the way in the development of innovative residential options (Mollica, Ladd, Dietsche, Wilson, & Ryther, 1992).

Expanding long-term care insurance
Most of the major health reform bills considered by the 103rd Congress placed a heavy emphasis on provisions to expand private long-term care insurance, including tax incentives to encourage the purchase of such policies and provisions allowing states to adopt the approach of the long-term care insurance demonstration states of expanding the use of public resources (i.e., Medicaid) to purchase insurance on behalf of prospective Medicaid, long-term care beneficiaries. Unfortunately, these provisions are not likely to significantly expand or improve rural long-term care. Despite increasing interest in private initiatives, and long-term care insurance in particular, as mechanisms for shifting the financial risk of long-term care away from public sources (i.e., Medicare and Medicaid), most observers believe that the high cost of most insurance products will limit the role of private insurance in long-term care (Wiener & Illston, 1994). The affordability of private long-term care coverage is an even greater problem in rural areas, where the rural elderly have lower incomes and where health insurance coverage has traditionally been lower (Schlenker & Shaughnessy, Chapter 7).

Cost containment
Despite a natural inclination to expand home care benefits and entitlements, policymakers are exceptionally nervous about the

cost implications of doing so. For this reason, all of the major bills considered in the 103rd Congress that expanded long-term care benefits did so within the framework of a capped entitlement program. The implications for rural long-term care of such financing limitations are potentially significant.

At issue is the distribution of long-term care resources between urban and rural people and places, and specifically, whether a capped entitlement could institutionalize any rural disadvantages that may exist in long-term care program funding and entitlements. Although there is limited research on this topic, Medicaid and other funding for aging and long-term care services is likely to be disproportionately low in rural areas relative to population-based needs, due to the limited availability of rural home care, rehabilitation and other critical services. Rural areas could be seriously disadvantaged by entitlement caps if, in establishing formulas for the distribution of resources, the federal government or the states did not appropriately redress current inequities in the distribution of resources and services. Rural areas will continue to face formidable financial challenges in building effective long-term care systems in the absence of policies to assure the equitable allocation of resources between urban and rural areas. Such assurances were not included in reform legislation.

Integrating primary, acute, and long-term care
There is a growing recognition of the interdependent nature of the primary and acute care sector and long-term care. This was reflected in some healthcare reform bills that would have expanded the Social/Health Maintenance Organization (S/HMO) and On-Lok-PACE experiments (American Association of Retired Persons [AARP], 1994). These experiments have demonstrated different insurance and service delivery approaches to integrating financing and service delivery systems to achieve better coordination of services and, presumably, more cost-effective acute and long-term care. These models seek to avoid unnecessary decline in functional status and to substitute outpatient care for costly inpatient services. In theory, savings associated with reductions in acute care

expenditures can be devoted to expanding community and home-based long-term care services.

The applicability of the S/HMO and PACE models, in their current form, may be limited in rural areas. Nevertheless, the concept of better integrating primary, acute and long-term care services holds considerable promise and may actually be able to be developed more easily in rural than urban areas. Although there are remote and frontier rural areas that lack appropriate access to a rural hospital or medical center, the majority of rural residents in this country live within reasonable proximity of such a facility. Rural hospitals have responded to declining acute care volume in recent years by expanding their long-term care services, starting with swing beds and, more recently, with home health, residential care (e.g., congregate housing, continuing care retirement communities) and other home- and community-based services (see Schlenker & Shaughnessy, Chapter 7).

It is unclear how the development and/or expansion of rural integrated service networks (ISNs) and managed care systems will affect the development of integrated acute and long-term care systems in rural communities. In theory, the expansion of networks and managed care systems into rural areas, either through linkages with larger urban-based systems or via locally based systems (there are currently very few locally based rural networks that function as managed care entities), could further the development of integrated primary, acute, and long-term care service systems. For many rural areas, however, chronic provider shortages and other well-known problems make the development of ISNs a significant challenge. It is unlikely that fragile rural networks will be interested in, or be able to, assume responsibility for a formal, integrated network of acute and long-term care services. This does not mean that greater integration cannot be achieved. To the contrary, as a number of observers have pointed out, less formal service coordination strategies may be more feasible in rural areas where there are fewer service providers, where there may be less competition and where communication among service providers may be easier (AARP 1994; see also Magilvy, Chapter 4).

Other Policy Provisions Affecting Rural Long-Term Care

There are at least two other issues which surfaced in the health reform debate in the 103rd Congress with significant implications for rural long-term care: (a) proposed changes in the Medicaid program and (b) proposed cuts in Medicare spending, which, in most bills, was a primary source of funding for insurance expansions and the new prescription drug and long-term care benefits. Most of the reform bills proposed substantially restructuring the Medicaid program by folding the Aid to Families with Dependent Children (AFDC) and noncash, AFDC-related beneficiaries into health plans offered through health insurance purchasing groups (i.e., "Alliances") with heavy public subsidies. The fate of dually eligible Medicare-Medicaid beneficiaries was uncertain in most of the reform proposals, however. It was unclear, for example, whether these individuals would be enrolled in managed health plans as Medicaid beneficiaries or excluded from such requirements by virtue of their status as Medicare beneficiaries. The implications for rural beneficiaries and providers could be significant. On the one hand, enrolling the dually eligible in mainstream managed care plans could promote better coordination among primary, acute and long-term care providers. Unfortunately, however, many rural primary and acute care providers may lack the experience and resources for managing the long-term care needs of their patients.

Proposed reductions in Medicare spending, which are likely to reappear if and when health reform returns to the policy agenda, would have had an even more significant effect on rural health systems and, indirectly, rural long-term care, than Medicaid revisions. Medicare represents a critical source of payment for most rural hospitals, which tend to have higher Medicare volumes than their urban counterparts. The proposed reductions in the prospective payment system (PPS) annual inflation updates might not have represented a significant problem for some rural hospitals that have shown improving profit margins over the past several years. The impact among rural Medicare-dependent hospitals, however, is likely to have been significant. Many of these facilities are already operating on borrowed financial time with little prospect for significant improvement. Between 1986 and 1989, an average of 40 hospitals closed each year. Since then, this number has dropped to approximately 30 per year. For the communities in which these hospitals are located, the hospital represents a critical asset in their efforts to develop or sustain a viable health service infrastructure. While it is unlikely, and perhaps unwise, to maintain these facilities as full-service acute care institutions, a planned transition to new health care provider roles as emergency access hospitals and/or as providers of long-term care would be far preferable to bankruptcy and closure.

THE IMPLICATIONS OF MARKET-DRIVEN HEALTH SYSTEM CHANGES FOR RURAL LONG-TERM CARE

There have been dramatic changes in recent years in the consolidation of health providers and systems into formal networks and managed care organizations. Reviews of these developments among health care providers and citizens are decidedly mixed, especially in rural communities. At one extreme there are those who fear the "balkanization" and takeover of fragile rural health systems by large, urban-based managed care companies. Others argue that the development of integrated service networks has the potential for helping rural and underserved communities develop a more stable and comprehensive health care infrastructure through consolidation and rationalization of existing services and by linking these communities to larger service systems (Christianson & Moscovice, 1993; Coburn & Mueller, 1995; Fuchs, 1994; Korczyk & Witte, 1991).

Although the crystal ball is particularly cloudy at this juncture, it seems clear that market-driven trends toward system consolidation and managed care are likely to continue. We can only speculate about the implications of these developments for rural long-term care. The development of rural integrated service networks may provide the administrative and clinical infrastructure needed to expand rural long-term care services. Combined with the growing population with chronic care needs, trends toward managed care, although less pronounced in rural areas, will nevertheless encourage the integration of primary, acute, and long-term care services.

The development of integrated managed care services covering both acute and long-term care has already captured the interest of federal and state policymakers concerned with improving service delivery and controlling Medicaid and Medicare expenditures for chronic care populations. A number of states, including Arizona and Minnesota, have developed or are developing managed long-term care systems for Medicaid recipients that build on HMO-based delivery systems used to deliver managed care to AFDC and other nondisabled Medicaid beneficiaries. Maine is similarly planning to move its elderly and disabled Medicaid beneficiaries into capitated, managed care systems. The experience of these states may provide important lessons regarding the potential impact in rural areas of these emerging managed acute and long-term care systems.

PROSPECTS FOR FUTURE REFORM

The prospects for comprehensive, national health care reform appear bleak; the prospects for significant long-term care reform (e.g., a meaningful home care entitlement program) appear even bleaker. It seems highly unlikely, given the current budget deficit, that Congress will be able to muster sufficient consensus to raise the $20–$30 billion necessary to fund such an entitlement program. Incremental reforms with, at best, only modest impact on rural long-term care, appear more likely. Under this scenario, state reform efforts will assume greater importance.

On the theory that policymakers will one day have to attend to what many believe is a looming long-term care crisis, what should we and others concerned with rural long-term care be advocating? The following represents a beginning list of critical issues that, if addressed in future health reform policy, could expand and improve rural long-term care.

Home- and Community-Based Services

An expansion of public funding for home- and community-based services, including residential, day care and respite facilities and services, is particularly vital to the development of rural long-term care in light of the lower purchasing capacity of the rural elderly. Flexibility in the definition of those services is particularly important in rural areas where everything from transportation to home repair and personal communication devices may be critical in developing a service package to meet a client's needs. Funding for these services could come from existing sources (e.g., the Rural Electrification Administration and the Department of Agriculture), or new sources (e.g., public subsidy or entitlement programs), as was proposed in health reform bills considered in the 103rd Congress.

Long-Term Care Infrastructure Improvements

While policies to increase the supply of long-term care services in rural areas are needed, infrastructural improvements will be critical to ensure that services can be provided efficiently and effectively. Incentives should be provided in existing and new programs to encourage rural communities and providers to develop integrated service models. Such incentives might include special demonstration program grants, technical assistance and/or reimbursement.

Capital financing may also be needed to support the development of appropriate residential, transportation, communication, service delivery or other facilities in more remote communities. Grants and other support for the development of appropriate communication technologies may be important for the development of effective service integration strategies.

Support and technical assistance in the development of health data systems will also be critical elements in any efforts to promote service integration across different provider systems and communities.

Rural Hospital and Nursing Home Transition Programs

In addition to schools, hospitals and nursing facilities often represent the principal capital structure in rural communities. As such, they are important building blocks for the development of rural long-term care systems (see Rowles, Chapter 6 and Schlenker & Shaughnessy, Chapter 7, in this volume). Both financial assistance and regulatory flexibility may be needed to enable these organizational entities to move into expanded roles in providing long-term care. On the hospital side, the federal Essential Access Community Hospital/Primary Care Hospital (EACH/PCH), Hospital Transition and Rural Outreach programs already provide assistance on a limited scale for this purpose.

Public, Consumer, and Provider Education and Training

Expanded provider education and training programs emphasizing geriatrics and long-term care, especially those targeted to nurses, primary care physicians, and allied health personnel, will be needed to support the development of effective rural long-term care systems. Getting these providers into rural and underserved areas and keeping them there is always a problem. Special incentives, such as grant programs and subsidies, may be needed to accomplish this goal.

Training programs targeted to PCAs and other paraprofessional service providers (including family members) will be needed to ensure the availability and quality of rural long-term care. Consumer education is also needed for clients and families to enable them to access and use community-based long-term care services.

Rural Representation in the Policy Process

In the final analysis, the sensitivity of policymakers and the policy process to rural interests in the debate over any long-term care reform will depend, in part, on the involvement of rural people and interests in the policy process. To date, rural involvement in the long-term care provisions of health reform has been minimal. This will have to change if we want future reform to be responsive to rural needs and problems.

REFERENCES

American Association of Retired Persons (AARP) and National Academy for State Health Policy. (1994). *Integrating acute and long-term care: Advancing the health care reform agenda.* Washington, DC: American Association of Retired Persons.

Beaulieu, J. E. (1994). Services for the rural elderly and disabled. In J. E. Beaulieu & D. Berry (Eds.), *Rural health services: A management perspective* (pp. 229–257). Ann Arbor, MI: Health Administration Press.

Christianson, J., & Moscovice, I. (1993). Health reform and rural health networks. *Health Affairs, 12*(3), 58–80.

Coburn, A. F., & Mueller, K., (1995). Legislative and policy strategies for supporting rural health network development: Lessons from the 103rd Congress. *The Journal of Rural Health, 11,* 22–31.

Fuchs, B. (1994). *Health care reform: Managed competition in rural areas.* Washington, DC: Congressional Research Service.

Kane, R. L., & Kane, R. A. (1987). *Long-term care: Principles, practices, programs and policies.* New York: Springer Publishing Co.

Korczyk, S. M., & Witte, H. A. (1991). *Managed care plans in rural America: How they work, what they do.* Report to the National Rural Electric Cooperative Association and the Metropolitan Life Insurance Company. Washington, DC: National Rural Electric Cooperative Association.

Mollica, R., Ladd, R., Dietsche, S., Wilson, K., & Ryther, B. (1992). *Building assisted living for the elderly into public long-term care policy: A technical guide for state health policy.* Portland, ME: National Academy for State Health Policy.

Rivlin, A., Wiener, J., Hanley, R., & Spence, D. (1988). *Caring for the disabled elderly: Who will pay?* Washington, DC: Brookings.

Shaughnessy, P. (1994). Changing institutional long-term care to improve rural health care. In R. T. Coward, C. N. Bull, G. Kukulka, & J. M. Galliher (Eds.), *Health services for rural elders* (pp. 144–181). New York: Springer Publishing Co.

Wiener, J., & Illston, L. (1994). Health reform in the 1990s: Where does long-term care fit in? *The Gerontologist, 34,* 402–408.

Long-Term Care for the Rural Elderly: Toward the Twenty-First Century

9

Joyce E. Beaulieu
Graham D. Rowles
Wayne W. Myers

In previous chapters of this volume, descriptions and analyses were presented on the long-term care needs of rural elders, the status of rural long-term care systems, the strengths of some emerging modes of service delivery, opportunities for developing the infrastructure of rural long-term care, and obstacles to the development of comprehensive long-term care systems. What emerges clearly is that long-term care of the elderly is currently undergoing significant change as, with increasing numbers of frail elders, new options are introduced and institutions adapt to the changing circumstances of rural America. In this chapter we provide an integration of these themes as we address the potential for developing community sensitive systems of rural long-term care.

The chapter is divided into three sections. First, we present seven guiding principles, consistent with contemporary directions in long-term care, that we believe should undergird the evolution of long-term care in rural America over the next two decades. Second, we speculate about ways in which adoption of these principles is likely to influence the evolution of the long-term care system as we move into the 21st century. We suggest that such a system is likely to differ in significant ways from the highly fragmented system of long-term care that currently exists in most rural areas. Third, we suggest a number of directions for research and advocacy that will facilitate informed innovation as we seek to develop comprehensive systems of community-sensitive rural long-term care.

GUIDING PRINCIPLES FOR RURAL LONG-TERM CARE

Seven principles are espoused to guide the development and improvement of long-term care for rural elders. These principles not only provide a template for service system analysis and development but also incorporate ethical and philosophical tenets that should guide payers, regulators, providers and researchers of rural long-term care, as well as the expectations of rural clients, their families and other advocates for improvement of current models of rural long-term care. Some of these principles are not unique to rural areas—they are applicable to both rural and urban long-term care services and clients. Others are already incorporated, either explicitly or implicitly, in the design and operation of selected contemporary rural service delivery systems. More conscious adoption of these principles is needed to compensate for a history of uncritical, inappropriate, and ineffective application of essentially urban models of long-term care to rural settings, under circumstances reflecting an obliviousness to rural needs and culture.

Community Locus of Control

Diversity among communities, a hallmark of rural America, is the bane of researchers and policymakers in their attempts to develop programs that are consistent and generalizable (Rowles, 1988). At one extreme lie *frontier* designations: communities with population densities of six or fewer people per square mile, and long driving distances or geographical barriers between health services. Many such communities are located in the mountain and intermountain regions of the West (Berry, Tucker, & Seavey, 1988). At the other extreme lie small bedroom communities situated outside designated metropolitan statistical areas (MSAs), but essentially serving as living quarters for workers in the MSA, who also do their shopping and generally obtain health services in the town where they work. Somewhere in the middle of these extremes of rurality are the stereotypical farming communities and small towns which most people think of when they use the term rural, but which comprise only 13% of the nonmetropolitan United States population (Miller, Farmer, & Clarke, 1994).

Accompanying the diversity in size of rural communities is wide variation in population characteristics, economic bases, cultures, and long-term care resources. A newly emergent rural retirement community will tend to have a healthier elderly population, with less demand for nursing home, hospital, and home health services, than will a rural community in which elders have aged in place, or one in which elders have returned home after living and working in industrial cities. On the other hand, communities characterized by aging in place may have strong family- and community-based informal support networks rich in lifelong associations and patterns of reciprocal obligation among families and generations (Lozier & Althouse, 1974). A frontier community may have a single source of health care: a small rural hospital supported by a local tax structure, providing swing-beds. Another rural community with a strong core of community development leaders may band together and build a nursing facility as its only health care institution, because several rural hospitals and a branch of the university medical school are accessible via interstate highways.

Dimensions of rurality which affect the types and breadth of a community's long-term care resources include (a) its historical supply of both acute and long-term health care (both institutional and noninstitutional services), (b) its economic strength (including both access to capital financing and the proportion of elders with coverage for long-term care), (c) the service development expertise available locally (e.g., health administrators, health planners, and attorneys and bankers with health services development experience), (d) the culture of its people and their propensity to use formal services or connect with "outsiders" rather than rely on indigenous "natural" support systems, (e) its geographic accessibility (travel time to urban centers with comprehensive health care resources), and (f) the "outreach" influence of urban health services in the form of managed care and integrated systems of care (Beaulieu, 1994).

Given the diversity of rural communities and long-term care resources that results from these factors, it is clear that decision making about the development of long-term care services and prioritization of long-term care needs should reside with community leaders, who are the real experts on the community, its specific needs and its resources. Just as it is folly to apply urban models to rural areas, it is folly to believe that there is one rural model that will fit all rural communities. Optimally, rural communities should have available to them the expertise to assess long-term care needs, resources, and service gaps, and to draw up appropriate plans for service development responding to their community's unique circumstances. Health planners and policymakers for rural communities should not be limited in their development activities to the strict service guidelines and requirements of categorical reimbursement and grant programs, whether based in urban models or rural models, but should be given flexible policy guidelines within which to work out local solutions to local problems. Within this rubric, local decision-making bodies, such as "community health councils" may provide the means for a community to invest in shaping its future.

Nonlinear Models of Care

The misnomer of "continuum" to characterize the menu of services for long-term care, while not strictly a rural problem, has far-ranging implications for rural services. The term unnecessarily creates an impression that elders progress along a linear life course, becoming increasingly debilitated over time and using services in a stepwise fashion along the continuum. Indeed, this model has become something of a self-fulfilling prophecy in long-term care program development. In reality, few people follow such a trajectory. An elder's health care life course is typically haphazard, with episodes of acute care hospitalization, short-term nursing facility stays, and periods of home care, all interspersed with periods of family or neighbor support. In addition, the presence of multiple illnesses, both acute and chronic, in the elderly, make predictions about the need for care difficult. It is also important to acknowledge that for many elders dependency in one domain of their lives (e.g., mobility) may increase, while they remain entirely independent in other domains (e.g., capacity for self-care). When formal services are unavailable or unaffordable, as is the case for many rural elders, the life course use of services becomes even more unpredictable.

Recognizing this complexity, models are needed which recognize fluctuating long-term care needs, acknowledge the fragmentary nature of rural service availability, accept the limited resource potential of most rural areas to create a complete continuum of care (Coward & Cutler, 1988), and attempt to reconcile these themes. Reconciling service needs and availability may be possible through the development of a multifaceted long-term care system that both acknowledges the constraining realities of the local resource base and is sensitive to local social and cultural expectations. Such a system must be flexible enough to incorporate long-term care trajectories that include phases of improvement, as well as decline. Growing recognition of the potential for innovative case management options in rural areas holds some promise in this regard (Parker et al., 1992a,b). Because of their administrative and financial structures, case management models for the elderly have the potential to integrate primary care with acute care and long-term care, to focus on the integrated needs of individual patients, and to provide for continuity of all levels of care over episodes of illness.

Client-Centered Philosophy of Care

Too often, health policy and health and social services reimbursement focus on historical categorical programs (e.g., Medicare and Medicaid) and existing health care institutions (e.g., hospitals, nursing facilities, home health agencies). Waivers for home- and community-based care under the Medicaid program restrict the types of eligible persons, the numbers of people who can be served in a fiscal year, and the types and amounts of services to be used. The swing-bed program under Medicare is restricted to recipients in hospitals of a certain size, meeting specific requirements for service provision. Medicare itself pays very little for long-term care, while many elders are forced to spend down to poverty levels to receive Medicaid-eligible services (Vladeck, Miller, & Clauser, 1993). In some rural communities, 80%–90% of a nursing facility's census may be Medicaid recipients, putting a financial burden on the nursing home in providing an appropriate level of services.

Given the prevalence of program-specific and institution-centered reimbursement mechanisms, individual clients' true needs may be ignored, as they are pigeonholed into available programs. Patterns of long-term care thus become program rather than person driven. More demonstrations and innovative service models are required that provide the flexibility to respond to the unique needs and circumstances of individual clients (Vladeck et al., 1993). The only reimbursement schemes which currently approach this philosophy are managed care types of reimbursement, such as social health maintenance organizations (S/HMOs), which combine acute and long-term care reimbursement streams into a single source. Such options acknowledge responsibility for a more comprehensive, client-centered approach to addressing long-term care needs. Currently, no S/HMO models are being tested in rural situations, although one is planned in rural New York State (G. M. Eggert, Personal communication, October 1994).

Family-Centered Decision Making

Just as the community should be the unit of responsibility in planning and providing services to meet community needs, so should the client and his or her family be considered the unit making decisions about the services they use. For most people, the family is the basic social unit providing the context for decision making. Family decision-making relationships become increasingly important to elderly persons who are cognitively compromised or threatened by disabilities requiring long-term care. In this context, family-centered decision making may be especially important to rural elders as it facilitates making long-term care choices that are sensitive to an individual's personal history and immediate social context. Family-centered needs for reciprocity, independence, and a degree of continuing autonomy permeate the lives of many rural elders. Such needs and preferences can be more appropriately represented when an individual's family is fully involved and is afforded the opportunity to provide input into critical long-term care decisions. As Stoller (Chapter 3) reminds us, family involvement should extend beyond making decisions for an older relative: It should involve the perpetuation of empowerment. Family members can consult with their older relatives and both encourage and enable elders to continue to do as much as possible for themselves.

Existing programs and agencies tend to have their own care plans or case managers who assess needs and draw up a "package" of services perceived to be relevant to the client's needs. Within this context, benign, but insidious, proxy decisions are often made on behalf of clients whose objective circumstances may be assessed but who remain relatively "unknown" as people. Such decisions, seemingly in the client's best interest, may result in a kind of paternalistic co-opting of the client and family. In the long run, case management, if not responsive to the needs and wishes of the client and his or her family, can be harmful, not only to the client, but, ultimately to the culture of rural elders, their dignity and their independence (Urv-Wong & McDowell, 1994). In interviews with rural case managers, flexibility with respect to the client's wishes, acknowledgment of the family context of many elder's lives, and the flexible use of resources have been described as hallmarks of successful rural service provision (Beaulieu & Hickman, 1988). Case managers also noted several vital attitudes: discarding their own personal judgments upon entering a client's house, acknowledging that they are often perceived as outsiders, and attempting to immerse themselves in the family milieu of each client.

Access to Information

In order for rural elders and their families to become informed consumers of long-term care, they need accurate, complete, and usable information about available programs and services, about resources available for financing care, and about options for developing alternative sources of support within their communities. Information needs to be accessible in a timely manner because long-term care decisions must often be made within a few hours of discharge from a hospital or nursing facility. Whenever nursing facility beds are not available in a rural community, or an excess demand for beds creates long waiting lists, clients and families should be aware of these situations before they are confronted with untenable solutions (for example, waiting without services until a bed becomes available, or being admitted to a facility located a considerable distance from their home community). Financial advising is required to aid clients in planning for appropriate care in appropriate amounts, given sound actuarial data. Educational programs for families are needed that teach them to identify early signs of debility in elders, to cope with caregiving tasks and burdens, to seek appropriate advice in the event of need for formal services, and to talk to elders about their wishes before irrevocable decisions are made on their behalf (such as "do not resuscitate" decisions). Finally, advocates for the elderly need access to information about gaps in services, barriers to service delivery and reimbursement, and options for better planning and integration of long-term care services.

Contrary to stereotypes, the need for information may actually be more acute in rural areas than in most urban settings. Many rural communities suffer from less efficient channels of communication, fewer informal meeting places for rural elders, and fewer health and social services for supporting rural elders and their families throughout the long-term care decision-making process (McKinley & Netting, 1994). While individual agencies may believe they now provide comprehensive clearinghouse information and referral services, they often are cognizant of only a small range of service options, a limited array of categories of eligibility, or only part of the health and social services "menu." A single, highly visible agency in each rural community needs to be responsible for the compilation of information and its dissemination to elders and their families in the community and in outlying rural areas, which are often overlooked by agencies "in town." Charging one agency with this responsibility can increase the possibility that information is efficiently duplicated, is accurate and complete, and reflects current services and rules of eligibility. Providers will then be able to identify a single agency as a central location through which to funnel information about their services, with assurance that the information will be readily accessible and available to potential clients and their families.

Cooperation Among Providers

Given the diversity of rural areas and the diversity of needs for long-term care, no single institution, agency, or organization can serve all the long-term care needs of rural populations. As a result, most rural areas are characterized by several institutions, agencies, or organizations that compete in providing long-term care. Due to the rules and regulations of individual reimbursement programs, providers often are pitted against one another in competition for the best paying patients, the highest reimbursement for services, and the best community image. This competition may produce unnecessary overlap in services, duplication of effort, lack of integrated community planning, and a maze of disconnected services through which clients and their families must find their way.

In opposition to the popular wisdom that everyone knows everyone's business in a rural community, rural providers often remain unaware of the range of each other's services. In part, this may be attributed to a lack of opportunities for networking and communication among rural providers, an absence of formal mechanisms for bringing rural providers together to discuss common issues, and the enmity that may build up between providers as they protect their turf—access to patients. The process of competition can be especially harmful with respect to developing an integrated system of long-term care. Small population bases, large proportions of Medicaid eligible clients, and the difficulties of recruiting and retaining health and social service professionals in rural communities may accentuate an environment of competition among a small group of providers. Additional pressure may be placed on the already strained resources of each agency as it independently pursues a natural imperative for survival.

In contrast to this scenario of competition is the cooperative spirit now emerging in some rural communities, as individual agencies and organizations begin to conduct comprehensive assessments of rural health needs, collaborative planning of health services, and cooperative service provision. For instance, the Appalachian Regional Healthcare (ARH) system, a network of rural nonprofit hospitals and health services in Appalachian Kentucky, West Virginia, and Virginia, has conducted several projects with local community leaders, planning for elders' needs (Calico, 1994). Facilities in ARH are not always the foci of service provision: Rather, in supporting such initiatives, ARH is lending its management expertise, pursuant to its general corporate goal of improving the health of the people in the communities within its service area.

Models of interinstitutional cooperation in addressing community needs should be encouraged wherever feasible in rural communities, communication systems among providers should be improved, and the divisions between acute and long-term care, and between medical and social services for elders (fostered by reimbursement and programmatic policies) should be reduced as much as is feasible (Bowlyow, 1990; see also Magilvy, Chapter 4 and Schlenker & Shaughnessy, Chapter 7, in this volume). Administrators of health and social services should be trained to understand community needs and to have a community orientation in their service planning efforts that transcends a sole focus on the survival and prosperity of their own institution or agency. Such training should incorporate a philosophical reorientation toward a broader vision of community need and an ethos of cooperation rather than of competition with other providers. Financial incentives to build coalitions in the community for the improvement of the overall long-term care system should be created. It is possible for institutions not only to survive, but also to thrive, through cooperative programming and service integration directed toward a shared vision of a comprehensive community-wide long-term care system. Indeed, we would argue that mechanisms should be developed to hold administrators accountable for such collaboration and outreach.

Redefinition of Health Professional Roles

While rural areas suffer from an inadequate supply of physicians and other health and social service professionals, they suffer even more acutely from the scarcity of some professionals providing long-term care, such as skilled nurses and rehabilitation therapists (Conway-Welch, 1991; Coward, Mclaughlin, Duncan, & Bull, 1994; Gesler & Ricketts, 1992; Hicks, 1990). In addition, access to some services, such as those reimbursed by Medicare, Medicaid, and many private insurers, is allowed only through the "gatekeeping" referral of a physician.

To reduce the dependence on physicians and to allay somewhat the scarcity of other professionals, rural areas should be allowed the flexible use of health professionals. Alternatives to exclusive physician control over referral to services should be instituted wherever feasible, thereby returning decision making to clients and their families, and reducing reliance on physicians. Cross-training of rehabilitation therapists should be allowed to help alleviate the need for multiple types of rehabilitation professionals: for example, physical therapists should be permitted to train in and provide occupational therapy. Expanding the roles of nurse practitioners (NPs) and physician assistants (PAs) and providing them with adequate reimbursement for providing care in long-term care settings or with chronic patients is a strategy that has been tested with some success in urban settings. The programmatic and reimbursement policies needed for these expanded roles should be more aggressively pursued for rural areas. Some provisions currently in use, such as the use of NPs and PAs in federally funded rural health clinics, could be expanded to long-term care settings, including nursing facilities and adult day health care centers. The creation of new types of health and social service personnel should also be explored as an option for rural areas. Such personnel could be community residents familiar with rural culture and sensitive to the needs of rural elders. For example, the Kentucky Homeplace Project trains "family health care advisors"-community residents who work with their peers to access necessary services (especially preventive health services), provide basic health education, and limit the use of unnecessarily expensive resources (e.g., the use of hospital emergency rooms for primary care). Health profession schools and programs are now providing more opportunities for rural training. This trend of increased responsiveness to rural health education needs, coupled with the development of additional incentives to practice in rural areas as advocated by Coward, Netzer and Peek (see Chapter 2), should be encouraged and supported by state and federal policies whenever possible.

TOWARD THE TWENTY-FIRST CENTURY

In the current highly volatile climate of long-term care program development and policy, predictions regarding the future are somewhat hazardous undertakings. Nonetheless, it is appropriate to conclude this book with some, perhaps optimistic, speculation regarding trends in rural long-term care as we approach the next century. Assuming that long-term care will develop according to the principles we have outlined, how might the optimal rural long-term care landscape look in 20 or 30 years? In order to be effective the long-term care system of the 21st century must evolve from the fragmented and partial system that exists today. We speculate that such a system would have the following characteristics.

Interdependence

First, we anticipate that the rural long-term care system of the future will manifest a high level of interdependence among its elements. Sophisticated and comprehensive health systems, like complex organisms, reveal a high level of functional interdependence. In the case of rural long-term care, formal health providers, informal caregivers, and the recipients of care would rely on each other, in a series of mutually interdependent reciprocal relationships, to build on strengths, shore up individual weaknesses, and provide the most appropriate care in an efficient manner. Following the precedent of acute care health systems, rural long-term care systems will be interdependent on urban systems for some resources, including administrative assistance (database maintenance, for example), specialty medical care for rural nursing home residents, and similar resources. The proliferation of health system networks and managed care is likely to blur the urban/rural boundary and will advance interdependence between urban and rural areas, and among providers of health and social services in these settings.

Diversity

A second feature of the effective rural long-term care system of the future is likely to be diversity. Interdependent rural long-term care systems will be as diverse as the communities in which they are found. Some will be built on a public utility model, where scarce resources are provided through a tax structure. Other communities will develop long-term care systems focused on services provided through a single available institution—a senior center, hospital or nursing home. Yet other systems will be voluntary, tied in with managed care networks based in other communities. Proximity to other providers, an imperative to address the different needs of diverse subsets of rural elders (e.g., African-Americans, elderly retiree in-migrants, those aging in place), and the distinctive culture of each rural locality and its elderly population, will necessitate contrasting responses in different communities.

Integration

Although interdependence fosters integration, it does not assure this outcome. Integration is the product of deliberate and genuine communication among providers of services, and among providers, consumers, and their families. Developing a comprehensive and integrated rural long-term care system providing an appropriate quantity, quality and mix of services, delivered in a manner that is consonant with local culture and values requires a commitment to collaborative problem solving. It requires more than simply forging a set of formal contracts and agreements among various actors in the long-term care system, although such relationships may be an important prerequisite. Rather, it necessitates a reorientation of underlying values and beliefs regarding the way in which a long-term care system should function. Essentially, this implies a shared vision of rural long-term care systems as comprising a web of fully interlocking options, rather than an aggregation of separate programs. In order for rural long-term care services of the future to be successful, they will need to be integrated across health and social service boundaries, across funding streams (Medicare, Medicaid, private insurance), across categorical programs, and across health care cultures (Rowles, 1991). While some programs and reimbursement sources will be formally integrated at the national level through legal and regulatory change, it will be incumbent upon policymakers at the state and local levels to integrate other programs and to nurture community-sensitive local long-term care systems.

Communication

The theme of communication is likely to be the central motif of effective long-term care in the next century. In this context, effectiveness is measured in terms of the availability of an array of options to cover all long-term care circumstances, with in unconstrained movement among different options as individuals' circumstances change. Long-term care in rural areas will succeed when providers communicate among themselves about the programs they offer, and with both actual and potential consumers. Success will also be facilitated by the existence of a single community focal point for information and referral for all long-term care providers, users, and advocates.

Both formal and informal communications will be enhanced by computer networks, the so-called information highway, by the need of managed care networks to understand community resources and use of those resources, and by the development of information systems designed specifically for rural long-term care provision. Computer and satellite communication will enhance outreach and education for clients and families. Advocates for the elderly will have comprehensive information available to them on health issues including illness prevention and health maintenance. Health professionals will have access to updated diagnostic and treatment information and avenues of patient data transmittal. On-site training of providers will be a feature of rural areas, and through the use of telemedicine and the relaying of medical and social service data via phone lines, rural patients will be able to stay in their community for diagnosis and treatment. The easy transfer of computerized patient records and widespread use of home monitoring systems will enhance the information available for home- and community-based care, thus facilitating home delivered treatments.

Innovation

The early 21st century is likely to be an era of innovation in rural long-term care. Innovation will be stimulated by strong local leaders exploring new alternatives in diverse rural settings—each setting providing a unique mix of resources and opportunities for innovation. Depending on the characteristics of each setting, innovation will be variously driven by the particular characteristics of local institutions (hospitals, nursing homes, senior centers, etc.), the needs of minority elders, the influx of large numbers of affluent retirees, changes in reimbursement and financing for long-term care, and local political considerations (Agency for Health Care Policy and Research, 1994).

The emergence of a variety of new long-term care options is almost inevitable; for example, new variants of short-term long-term care are likely to develop as hospitals and nursing homes evolve in the direction of subacute care and assume new roles within the rural health care system. There are likely to be new types of health personnel who have graduated from innovative rurally based and rurally integrated educational programs. Services will become demand driven as more consumers accrue the financial means, retirement incomes, and desire to use formal services. Given the higher levels of education of the current population in age group 40–60, consumers of rural long-term care in the 21st century will be more activist and more discriminating. They will likely demand more services that meet their needs for autonomy, privacy, and independence. Funding mechanisms are likely to be very different than they are today, as the Social Security fund and Medicare are revamped or dismantled, and more private funding schemes are developed.

Quality

The emphases of innovation will be on cost-effective long-term care services that result in measurably improved physical, mental, and social functioning. Obviously, innovation will succeed if it meets the needs of clients and their families, and results in outcomes superior to those obtainable from current services. For the remainder of this century and in the early 21st century, an outcomes orientation is likely to pervade the nation's entire health care system. In rural long-term care, information to document outcomes, techniques for measuring outcomes over a long period of time, and the personnel to provide high-quality services to ensure positive outcomes, will be required. Quality will be gauged in terms of outcomes that meet rural clients' and families' needs for timeliness, access in remote areas, personalized, private services, and the continuation of client independence and autonomy.

RESEARCH AND ADVOCACY

Without thorough, well-designed, and perceptive research into rural long-term care, movement toward the ideal with respect to rural long-term care systems will be long in coming. The advent of computer networks of communication, the growing role of telemedicine, and improved training of health professionals in rural communities can all increase the visibility of long-term care issues. Increased visibility will, in turn, increase the probability that more research will be undertaken on rural long-term care. Such research, including both quantitative and qualitative studies, is essential for system improvement. An ongoing cycle of basic research, research-based program innovation, evaluation research, and subsequent program modification and refinement can thus be initiated. Through this process, the best examples of rural long-term care systems can be communicated to rural leaders to assist them in system analysis and improvement. Information on successful models of rural policy in different states must be shared with communities contemplating innovation in long-term care service development. Partnerships between rural communities and universities should be fostered to aid in the development of rural research, to establish demonstration programs of long-term care, to provide training of health and social service professionals in rural communities and health facilities, and to enhance the flow of new information to community leaders.

It is beyond the scope of this chapter to present specific research strategies that will increase our understanding of rural long-term care and provide the database for innovation. However, the following research questions, while not claiming to be comprehensive, provide an initial agenda for rural long-term care research. The questions are organized within the rubric of the five major rural institutions that have been the focus of this book: the family, home- and community-based services, senior centers, nursing homes, and hospitals.

Rural Families

1. What are the dynamics of family discussions concerning long-term care?

2. What are family expectations with regard to long-term care?

3. How do family-based long-term care support systems (involving siblings, neighbors, and other informal caregivers) develop and function on a daily basis? How do these

systems accommodate to changes in the circumstances of care recipients and caregivers?

4. What is the economic impact of caregiving for rural caregivers?

5. What are the most effective methods for educating rural families about long-term care needs and services?

6. What is the relationship between families and formal caregiving organizations and how do families interact with such organizations?

Home- and Community-Based Services

1. What is the role of elders as providers and as the focus of self-help networks?

2. At what point and under what conditions do rural residents decide to supplement informal care with formal services?

3. What services do rural residents use and why do they utilize these particular services and avoid others?

4. What is the true cost differential between home-based and institution-based long-term care services to rural clients at different acuity levels?

5. What are the characteristics of communities and programs that successfully provide innovative home- and community-based services?

6. What role does local entrepreneurship play in the development of integrated rural home- and community-based long-term care programs?

Rural Senior Centers

1. To what extent do rural senior centers currently serve as resources for the provision of long-term care?

2. What are the characteristics of senior centers in rural areas

that successfully provide information about or offer long-term care services?

3. What aspects of long-term care provision can and cannot be carried out effectively and efficiently by senior centers?

Rural Nursing Homes

1. What is the supply and cost of rural and urban nursing home beds in different states and how do the characteristics of rural nursing homes differ from urban nursing homes?

2. How does the optimal number of nursing home beds for rural areas vary with demography and culture?

3. What decision-making process do families use in making the transition from home to a rural nursing home facility or from one level of care to another?

4. How and to what extent do transitions in and out of nursing homes and the outcomes of nursing home placement and care differ between rural and urban settings?

5. To what extent are campus model rural nursing homes currently being developed? What are the advantages and drawbacks of such models?

Rural Hospitals

1. What are the distinctive characteristics of rural hospitals, hospital administrators and communities that provide successful long-term care services?

2. What innovative strategies are being or can be demonstrated in rural hospital-based long-term care, aside from the currently documented swing-bed program, distinct skilled nursing facility units, and hospital-based home health programs?

3. What reimbursement changes in Medicare and Medicaid are

necessary to enable hospitals to effectively provide long-term care in rural areas?

4. What are the appropriate criteria for assessment of quality in hospital-based rural long-term care?

It should be emphasized that many of these questions straddle several institutional categories and are interdependent. Thus, each question should be viewed as potentially casting light on the functioning of the entire system of long-term care. As with most systems, many of the most challenging questions pertain to relationships among the different components of the fragmented and incomplete long-term care system. Research providing clearer understanding of such relationships will provide a baseline for addressing a series of more general issues with critical implications for the future of long-term care in rural America—issues ranging from the appropriate placement of subacute short-term long-term care services (in hospitals? nursing homes? or some new type of facility?), through the role of rehabilitation rather than maintenance as a central motif of rural long-term care, to consideration of optimal ways of financing comprehensive systems of care.

Not all research and demonstrations need be initiated by governmental sources. Many gerontological foundations, private health corporations, and private individuals have a stake in the continued success of rural long-term care. For instance, a multi-institutional system of nursing facilities that owns and operates nursing homes in several rural communities wants its facilities to thrive, and has a need for community participation. Demonstrating new facility-community partnerships in several of its rural facilities would serve both purposes. State and regional gerontological societies provide fertile ground for discussion and debate on rural long-term care issues, because their memberships are often drawn from smaller communities, and tend to include researchers, health, aging, and social service practitioners, and consumer advocates for the elderly.

CONCLUSIONS

Our discussion of a desirable future for long-term care for the rural elderly has an admittedly optimistic tone. It suggests a number of directions in which we need to advance in order to replace ad hoc, fragmented, and partial systems of long-term care that have performed poorly with more comprehensive and holistic systems of long-term care that are attuned to rural community needs, resources, and cultures. Most important, in the context of the fizzling of health care reform initiatives on the national level, leaders of rural communities must take it upon themselves to make long-term care a priority. They must take the initiative in fostering renewed debates about long-term care policy at the local and state levels. Those who ultimately are the consumers must become advocates for health system change. Unless leaders and advocates push rural long-term care to prominence as an agenda item in a reinvigorated health policy debate, it is likely to be buried under health policy discussions regarding acute care funding for urban populations.

We acknowledge that in many rural states and rural communities the resources and expertise needed to propel rural long-term care to the front of the policy agenda, and to facilitate the development of the integrated and comprehensive programs of community-sensitive long-term care that we envisage, are currently lacking. In an era of fiscal constraints the challenge lies in mustering the resources to effect change. However, without a vision of the possible, change is likely to be, at best, haphazard, and those who grow old and frail in rural communities are likely to find their meager support diminishing even further.

ACKNOWLEDGMENTS

Some material in this chapter is adapted from a position paper, *Contemporary Directions in Long-term Care for the Rural Elderly*, that resulted from a conference on "Long-term Care for the Rural Elderly" sponsored by the Agency for Health Care Policy and Research and held in Lexington, Kentucky, on September 23–24,

1994. We would like to acknowledge the contributions to this position paper of David Bolt, Forrest Calico, Patricia A. Calico, Malcolm P. Cutchin, Deborah D. Danner, Ruth R. Davis, Dallas M. High, John A. Krout, Linda C. Kuder, Cynthia A. Leedham, Jim McAuley, B. Jan McCulloch, Barbara Kopp Miller, Julie Netzer, James Norton, Chuck W. Peek, Linda Redford, Bill Remmes, Robert E. Schlenker, Peter Shaughnessy, and Diana West.

REFERENCES

Agency for Health Care Policy and Research. (1994, October/November). AHCPR launches major rural health research initiative. *Research Activities, 179,* pp. 11–12.

Beaulieu, J. E. (1994). Services for the rural elderly and disabled. In J. E. Beaulieu & D. E. Berry (Eds.), *Rural health services: A management perspective* (pp. 229–257). Ann Arbor, MI: Health Administration Press.

Beaulieu, J. E., & Hickman, M. (1988). Rural case management: A pilot study. *Home Health Care Services Quarterly, 14*(4), 71–87.

Berry, D. E., Tucker, T. C., & Seavey, J. (1988). Frontier hospitals: Endangered species and public policy issue. *Hospital and Health Services Administration, 33*(2), 61–75.

Bowlyow, J. E. (1990). Acute and long-term care linkages: A literature review. *Medical Care Review, 10*(3/4), 75–103.

Calico, F. (1994, September). *Innovative rural long-term care.* Presentation at National Conference, "Long-Term Care for the Rural Elderly." Lexington: KY.

Conway-Welch, C. (1991). Issues surrounding the distribution and utilization of nurse and nonphysician providers in rural America. *Journal of Rural Health, 7*(Suppl.), 388–401.

Coward, R. T., & Cutler, S. J. (1988). The concept of a continuum of residence: Comparing activities of daily living among the elderly. *Journal of Rural Studies, 4,* 159–168.

Coward, R. T., McLaughlin, D. K., Duncan, R. P., & Bull, C. N. (1994). An overview of health and aging in rural America. In R. T. Coward, C.

N. Bull, G. Kukulka, & J. M. Galliher (Eds.), *Health services for rural elders* (pp. 1–32). New York: Springer Publishing Co.

Gesler, W. M., & Ricketts, T. C. (1992). *Health in rural North America: The geography of health care services and delivery.* New Brunswick, NJ: Rutgers University Press.

Hicks, L. L. (1990). Availability and accessibility of rural health care. *Journal of Rural Health, 6,* 485–505.

Lozier, J., & Althouse, R. (1974). Social enforcement of behavior toward elders in an Appalachian mountain settlement. *The Gerontologist, 14,* 69–80.

McKinley, A. H., & Netting, F. E. (1994). Information and referral: Targeting the rural elderly. In J. A. Krout (Ed.), *Providing community-based services to the rural elderly* (pp. 23–41). Thousand Oaks, CA: Sage.

Miller, M. K., Farmer, F. L., & Clarke, L. L. (1994). Rural populations and their health. In J. E. Beaulieu & D. E. Berry (Eds.), *Rural health services: A management perspective* (pp. 3–26). Ann Arbor, MI: Health Administration Press.

Parker, M., Quinn, J., Viehl, M., McKinley, A., Polich, C. L., Detzner, D. F., Hartwell, S., & Korn, K. (1992a). Case management in rural areas: Definition, clients financing, staffing and service delivery issues. *Journal of Nursing Administration, 22*(2), 54–59.

Parker, M., Quinn, J., Viehl, M., McKinley, A., Polich, C. L., Hartwell, S., Van Hook, R., & Detzner, D. F. (1992b). Issues in rural case management. *Family and Community Health, 14*(4), 40–60.

Rowles, G. D. (1988). What's rural about rural aging? An Appalachian perspective. *Journal of Rural Studies, 4,* 115–124.

Rowles, G. D. (1991). Changing health culture in rural Appalachia: Implications for serving the elderly. *Journal of Aging Studies, 5,* 375–389.

Urv-Wong, E. K., & McDowell, D. (1994). Case management in a rural setting. In J. A. Krout (Ed.), *Providing community-based services to the rural elderly* (pp. 65–89). Thousand Oaks, CA: Sage.

Vladeck, B. C., Miller, N. A., & Clauser, S. (1993). The changing face of long-term care. *Health Care Financing Review, 14*(4), 5–23.

Index

SP *Springer Publishing Company*

HEALTH SERVICES FOR RURAL ELDERS

Raymond T. Coward, MSW, PhD,
C. Neil Bull, PhD, **Gary Kukulka,** PhD,
and **James A. Galliher,** PhD, Editors

This volume reviews and critiques the current state of health services delivery to rural elders. The authors identify "action agenda" which describes endeavors that can be undertaken to improve the health care of older persons living in small towns and rural communities. This book has been developed for social gerontologists,

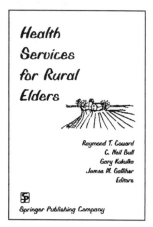

health care providers, and health services researchers committed to the improvement of health care for rural elders.

Partial Contents:

- Informal Care of Rural Elders, *R.P. Stoller and G.R. Lee*
- In-Home Services for Rural Elders, *G.M. Nelson*
- Rural Aging Community-Based Services, *J.A. Krout*
- Rural Hospitals and Rural Elders, *R.P. Duncan*
- Changing Institutional Long-Term Care to Improve Rural Health Care, *P.W. Shaughnessy*
- Mental and Social Health of the Rural Elderly, *K.C. Buckwalter, M. Smith, and C. Caston*
- Rural Aging Community-Based Services, *J.A. Krout*

1994   304pp   0-8261-8340-9   hardcover

536 Broadway, New York, NY 10012-3955 • (212) 431-4370 • Fax (212) 941-7842